# Simple Solutions

## English Grammar & Writing Mechanics

## level 6

Nancy McGraw & Nancy Tondy

**Bright Ideas Press, LLC**
**Cleveland, Ohio**

**Simple Solutions** *level 6*

**Grammar & Writing**



Printed in the United States of America

ISBN: 0-9772584-4-0

*Cover Design:* Tim Naujoks

*Editor:* Kimberly A. Dambrogio, NBCT



Cleveland, Ohio

# Welcome to Simple Solutions

**Note to the Student:**

*We hope that this program will help you understand English Grammar & Writing Mechanics concepts better than ever. For many of you, it will help you to have a more positive attitude toward learning these skills.*

*Using this workbook will give you the opportunity to practice skills you have learned in previous grades. By practicing these skills each night, you will gain confidence in your reading, writing and speaking ability.*

*In order for this program to help you, it is extremely important that you do a lesson every day. It is also important that you ask your teacher for help with the items that you don't understand or that you get wrong on your homework.*

*We hope that through Simple Solutions™ and hard work, you discover how satisfying and how much fun Language can be!*

## Lesson #1

1. **A noun names a person, place, thing, or idea.** Sort these nouns into one of the categories below.

   teacher justice Florida compass clock time Utah Dr. Rogers

| Person | Place | Thing | Idea |
|---|---|---|---|
| teacher | Utah | clock | time |
| Dr. Roger | Florida | compass | Jastice |

2. **A verb tells the action or condition of the subject in a sentence.** Underline two verbs in this sentence.

   The sisters sat on damp cedar logs and gazed into the darkness.

3. **Every sentence has a subject and a predicate; the subject tells whom or what the sentence is about.** Underline the subject in this sentence.

   The cupcakes are on the bake sale table.

4. Every sentence has a ___capital___ and a ______________.

5. After several days the flood waters began to abate, and people were able to return to their homes. What is the meaning of the underlined words?

   (A) fade away B) overwhelm C) damage D) engulf

6. The suffixes *–ible* and *–able* both mean "able to" or "able to be" (likeable, convertible, erasable). Underline the word that means "able to be applied."

   attractable accessible admissible applicable

7. **Place *i* before *e*, except after *c* or when sounded like *ā* as in neighbor and weigh. Examples:** believe freight receive Choose the missing letters.

   The coach will bring in a rel_ei_f pitcher now. ie ei

8. **Capitalize the first word in every sentence, including sentences within quotation marks.** **Example:** My favorite quote is by Mahatma Gandhi: "You must be the change you want to see in the world."
Which word should be capitalized in this sentence?

Gandhi also said, "you must not lose faith in humanity." ______

9 – 12. Brainstorming is a way to get ready for writing. Brainstorm a list of classes that you think should be offered at your school but are not (examples: Skateboarding Techniques, Drum Making, and Swahili).

I like to learn to do stateboard trix

______

______

______

______

# Lesson #2

## The Four Sentence Types

| Declarative | Interrogative | Imperative | Exclamatory |
|---|---|---|---|
| Statement | Question | Command / Request | Strong Emotion |
| ends in a period | ends in question mark | ends in a period | ends in an exclamation point |
| This is a sentence. | Is this correct? | Don't touch the wet paint. | This is awesome! |

1. Let's review the four sentence types. Study the chart above. Which type of sentence is this?

   It is fascinating to watch people at the bus stop. end in a period

2. Every sentence has a capital and a ____________.

3. Insert the letter of the word that correctly completes this sentence.

   You can see the Tampa Bay Devil Rays at Tropicana ________.

   A) field (B) Field C) Feild D) feild

4. **Use this editing mark ( ≡ ) under a letter to show that it should be capitalized.** Insert the editing mark.

   we can learn so much by studying the life of Mahatma Gandhi.

5. **A noun can be common or proper, singular or plural, or possessive, or any combination of these.** Underline four nouns in this sentence.

   Mrs. Florence gave my sister jellybeans that were made in France.

   possessive

6. **The verb is the main word found in the predicate.** Underline the verb (action word) in this sentence.

   Marquetta dances at festivals.

7. **Words can provoke certain feelings or reactions. This is called the word's connotation.** What is the connotation of the underlined word?

In many African stories Anansi the spider is a <u>con artist</u>.

trickster villain story-teller insect

8. The connotation of a word can be "soft" or "harsh." Underline the word that you think has the softest connotation.

Your painting is very (unusual / bizarre).

9. **Every sentence must close with an end mark: period, question mark, or exclamation point.** Use this editing mark (⊙) to show that an end mark is needed.

Try to open the door with this key

10. **The subject of a sentence must agree with the verb. A singular subject must have a singular verb; present tense singular verbs usually end in** *–s*.
**Example:** The puppy plays. Choose the correct verb.

The umbrella (open /opens) automatically.

11. Match these subjects with their verbs. sleeps survive

Animals sleep ____________. Nathan survive ____________.

**Proof It!** Use two different editing marks to correct errors in the following sentence.

12. After lunch, we will meet in mr. Williams' room

# Lesson #3

1. What are the four types of sentences?

staying in school

2. **Let's review.** See if you can match these meanings to the prefixes and suffixes listed in the chart.

not again before full of without

| | |
|---|---|
| A) | *re-* (refried, recreate, reiterate) |
| B) | *-ful* (hopeful, restful, playful) |
| C) | *-less* (penniless, wireless, timeless) |
| D) | *un-* (unbelievable, undo, untrained) |
| E) | *pre-* (precooked, pretest, prejudge) |

3. **There are some exceptions to every rule.** Here are some exceptions to the "*i* before *e*" rule: neither leisure foreign ancient
Write these words on the line below.

neither leicher foreign acient

4. **Proper nouns, proper adjectives, and the pronoun *I* are always capitalized.** Use the editing mark for capitalization to correct three errors in this sentence.

I love to eat indian food, but i have never been to asia.

5. **A plural subject must have a plural verb; present tense plural verbs usually do not end in *-s*.** Choose the correct verb.

The people (cheer / cheers) when the players come onto the field.

6. **The connotation of a word can be positive or negative.** Choose the word with the most positive connotation.

I really (envy / admire) Wayne's math ability.

7. **A proper noun names a particular person, place, thing, or idea; a proper noun always begins with a capital letter**. Underline the proper nouns in the following sentence.

   Jamaal and Darcy enrolled in a robotics class at the Corn Institute last summer.

8. **An action verb tells what the subject does or did**. Which sentence uses an action verb?

   A) Kenny *walked* fast. B) He *seemed* angry.

9 – 12. Writing a Course Description

   Choose one of the examples from your brainstorming in Lesson #1, and describe the class here. Explain what topics will be covered, what materials will be used, and what assignments will be given.

   Jamaal and Darcy enrolled in a robotics clas at the Corn Institute last summer.

## Lesson #4

1. At holiday times we <u>indulge in</u> sweets. Which of these means the <u>opposite</u> of the underlined part? (Use a dictionary if you need help.)

   A) gather together B) abstain from C) take apart D) treat ourselves

2. Which type of sentence is this?

   Who was the 15th president of the United States?

   Declarative Interrogative Imperative Exclamatory

3. **A pronoun takes the place of a noun.** A singular pronoun refers to one person, place, or thing. A plural pronoun names more than one person, place, or thing. Sort these pronouns into three groups: singular, plural, either.

   we I you us it she them your they he yours

   Singular ➡ I ride my bike to the park.

   Plural ➡ You going to kill yourself if you go down Here

   Either ➡ can you go with us

4. Choose the missing letters.

   My n___ce is my sister's daughter. ie ei

5. Use the editing mark for capitalization to mark two errors in this sentence.

   the alaskan husky is a large dog.

6. **A noun may be made up of more than one word. Examples:** Lauren McAllister, curling iron, Mount Union Underline all the nouns in this sentence.

   The Community Center is sponsoring a parade on Independence Day.

7. Choose the verbs that agree with the subject.

   The cheerleaders (wear / wears) blue sweaters and (carry / carries) yellow pom-poms.

8. **Let's review.** See if you can match these meanings to the prefixes and suffixes listed in the chart.

in a certain way not able to opposite of wrong

| | |
|---|---|
| A) sensible | *-ible* (sensible, flexible, divisible) |
| B) nonstop | *non-* (nonstop, nonskid, nonmetal) |
| C) misdeed | *mis-* (misjudge, misdeed, misstep) |
| D) disrespect | *dis-* (disregard, disobey, disrespect) |
| E) sadly | *-ly* (merrily, sadly, easily) |

9. ***Verbs of being*** **are non-action verbs; they name a** ***condition*** **or tell how the subject** ***is*****. Example:** The costumes *were* right here!
Look in the *Help Pages* for a list of the *Verbs of being*; write them here.

The costumes w^h^'re right here!

10. Remember, a **cause** tells *why*; an **effect** tells *what*. Is the underlined part a **cause** or an **effect**?

<u>The radio announcers predicted that the concert would sell out.</u> Consequently, there was a long line as soon as the tickets went on sale.

cause (circled) effect

11. Look in a dictionary or thesaurus and find a better word for *funny*. Write four synonyms for *funny*.

________________________________________

12. Choose an antonym for the underlined word. One <u>benefit</u> of our new housing development is that it is close to the freeway.

advantage <u>disadvantage</u> innovation construction

## Lesson #5

1. A ___sentence___ names a person, place, or thing.

2. Words containing *-phone* as in *telephone*, have to do with ________.

   light    sound    earth    form

3. **A sentence fragment is missing either a subject or a predicate.** Which is missing from this fragment?

   The house that I grew up in.    subject    predicate

4. Add what is missing, and rewrite the fragment above as a complete sentence.

   The house that I grew up in.

5. **A pronoun may refer to one or more nouns. The noun that the pronoun stands for is called the *antecedent*.** In the sentence below, the pronoun is in bold print; underline the antecedent.

   As soon as Marcie arrived at home, **she** checked the mailbox.

6. Match each pronoun with an antecedent.    us    he    she    them

   the boys ➡ ___them___    Deidre and I ➡ ___them___

   T.J. ➡ ___he___    Rita ➡ ___she___

7. **An interjection is a word or a phrase that shows emotion (surprise, relief, fear, or anger). Example:** Ouch! You dropped that on my toe.
   Interjections should be used sparingly – they are not usually appropriate for formal writing. Underline the interjection.

   Good grief! Can you be a little more careful?

8. **If a word has only one syllable or is stressed on the last syllable, double the final consonant when adding a suffix that begins with a vowel.**
**Example:** stop ➡ stoppable Write the word with its suffix.

plan + -er ➡ planable

9. This editing mark tells you to take out something. ( ) Use the editing mark to show what needs to be taken out of this sentence.

The price of gasoline it is so high these days!

10. Use the editing marks for capitalization and punctuation to edit this sentence.

My mother and i have begun to ride our bicycles to work

11 – 12. Now that you have edited two sentences, write them correctly on the lines below.

My Mother and I have begun to ride our bicycles to work.

## Lesson #6

1. A pronoun takes the place of a Japanse.

2. Draw a line through the sentence fragment.

   The fireworks were loud. But they were beautiful. Soaring across the night sky. We really enjoyed the show!

3. What is missing from the fragment in the item above --- subject or predicate?

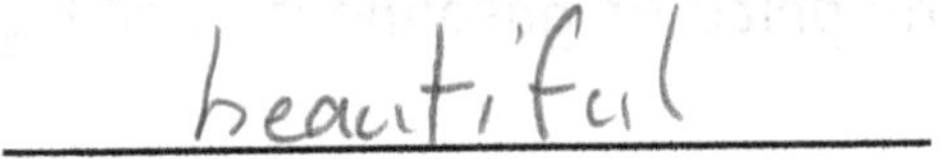

beautiful

4. Put a ✓ next to any prefix that means "not."

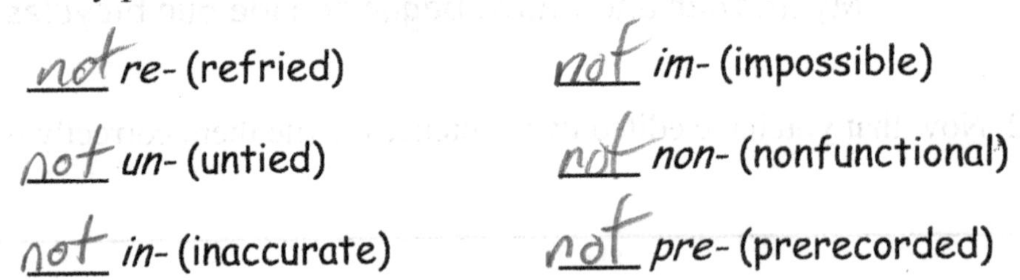

not *re-* (refried) not *im-* (impossible)

not *un-* (untied) not *non-* (nonfunctional)

not *in-* (inaccurate) not *pre-* (prerecorded)

5. Write these words with their suffixes.

   hot + -er ➡ hoter

   run + -ing ➡ runing

6. **A plural pronoun may have more than one antecedent.** Underline the antecedents of the pronoun *they*.

   Louis and his two brothers built the structure that they used for meetings.

7. **Memorize the *verbs of being* (forms of *be*).**
   Say the verbs like a cheer "is - are - was - were - be - am - being - been."
   Repeat the cheer until you have memorized the verbs.

8. A sentence may begin with an interjection. **Insert a comma after an interjection at the beginning of a sentence.** **Example:** Wow, the stadium is packed. Add the comma to this sentence.

Whew, here are our seats.

9. Study the definitions and choose the correct homophone to complete each sentence.

affect ➡ (*verb*) to influence or act upon

effect ➡ (*noun*) end result or (*verb*) cause

A) Tamara's plans should not (affect / effect) your decision.

B) Tamara will be responsible for the (affect / effect) of her actions.

10. Write an appropriate pronoun next to each antecedent.

you he she they it we

Matt and I ➡ they

the Millers ➡ we

the café ➡ it

11. This is the editing mark for "check spelling;" ( sp ) use it to mark two spelling errors in the following sentence.

The sign says, "To much of a good thing is grate!"

12. Write the eight ***verbs of being*** that you memorized. Try not to look back!

The signs says, "To much of a good thing graded."

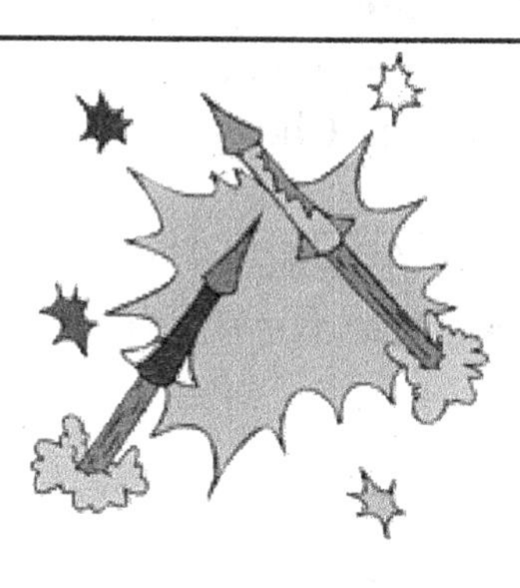

## Lesson #7

1. Find the meaning and pronunciation of the word *hearth* in a dictionary. Place a ✓ next to the statement that is true.

 ____ Hearth rhymes with "earth."

 ____ A hearth is part of a fireplace.

 ____ A hearth is part of a basement.

2. **If a word ends in a vowel and single consonant, double the final consonant when adding a suffix that begins with a vowel.**
 **Example:** control ➡ controller  Write the word with its suffix.

 expel + -ed ➡ expeledller

3. **An interjection may stand alone and is punctuated by an exclamation point.**
 **Examples:** Oh, no! We're late. Ouch! Don't push. (Notice that the next word—after the exclamation point—begins with a capital letter.)
 Put an exclamation point after the interjection.

 Oh my!_ The garden has been taken over by weeds.

4. **The complete subject includes the simple subject and all modifying words.**
 **Example:** Two dozen large doughnuts were in the box.
 Underline the complete subject.

 Delicious fresh squeezed orange juice was served at breakfast.

5. What is the meaning of the prefix *inter-*? (interdependent, intercede, intercellular)

 form  speak  not  between

6. A **pronoun must agree with its antecedent.** For example, if the antecedent is plural the pronoun must be plural; if the antecedent is feminine, the pronoun must be feminine. Choose the pronoun that agrees with the underlined antecedent.

 Kent and Jean traveled here from Tennessee; I think (they / he / she) came the furthest.

7. In this sentence one of the pronouns does not agree with its antecedent. Rewrite the sentence correctly. (Hint: Harlan is studying the French language, not French people.) Harlan is studying French because he likes the way they sound.

Harlan is studying french because he likes the way they sound.

8. Which sentence contains an action verb?

1 Ms. Alexander teaches at the university.

2 She is a full-time faculty member.

9. Draw a line through the fragment.

Once upon a time. Ancient civilizations flourished in isolated places.

10. Use the editing mark for capitalization to mark any errors in this sentence.

There is a vietnamese restaurant on lee road.

11 – 12. These sentences have been edited; write them correctly below.

Jessica and Andrew participated in the special Olympics this year

They wear both on the soccer team also.

Jessica and Andrew participated in the Special Olympics this year.

## Lesson #8

1. **Proper nouns name specific persons, places, or things**. Underline the proper nouns.

   Nicole and I visited the Garfield Monument with Mr. Levers.

2. A proper noun always begins with a Capital Letter.

3. Write these words with their suffixes.

   actual + -ly ➡ actually

   submit + -ing ➡ submiting

4. Write A for "action" or B for "being" to tell which kind of verb is used in each sentence.

   A The berries are ripe. A Let's pick them now.

5. **The subject pronouns are: I, you, he, she, it, we, you, and they.** Write a sentence using one of the subject pronouns.

   They went to a field trip.

6. Underline the complete subject.

   My favorite novel is *The Phantom Tollbooth* by Norman Juster.

7. Which prefix means "after?"

   auto- geo- mono- anti- post-

   monoafter

8. **The pronoun-antecedent relationship must be clear.**
**Example:** I left my jacket on the bus, but now I don't see it. (What is "it" — the jacket or the bus?) Rewrite the sentence clearly; do not use a pronoun.

I left my jacket on the bus, but now I don't see it.

9. **An interjection within a sentence is followed by a comma.** **Example:** Ah, that breeze feels wonderful! Add a comma after each interjection.

Oops! I dropped some sauce on the floor.

Hey! where is that stain remover for the carpet?

10. Remember, a **cause** tells *why*; an **effect** tells *what*. Is the underlined part a **cause** or an **effect**?

Chelsea had a severe overbite. So, she had to get braces.

cause effect

11. Which type of sentence is this?

Norman Juster was an architect, but he enjoyed writing novels in his spare time.

Declarative Interrogative Imperative Exclamatory

12. Use three different editing marks to fix these sentences.

Noreen was born in melbourne, Australia, Her family

moved here when she ever was ten.

## Lesson #9

1. Are the underlined words synonyms or antonyms?

   Narayan is adept at geometry but he seems baffled by algebra.

   synonyms antonyms

2. In which group are all the words spelled correctly?

   A) commitment, trotting, explained
   B) committment, trotting, explained
   C) commitment, troting, explained
   D) committment, trotting, explained

3. What is the meaning of the root *-port-*? (portable, transportation, portal)

   carry speak light within

4. **An apostrophe is used with the letter *-s* to show possession.**
   **Example:** Andy's cap Add an apostrophe wherever needed.

   I borrowed my moms car to pick up the supplies for Bobbys party.

5. Complete the sentence with a subject pronoun that agrees with the antecedent.

   Laura and I make bracelets; ____________ sell them at craft fairs.

6. Place a ✓ next to the sentence that contains an action verb.

   ____ Ashley was eight years old on her last birthday.
   ____ She celebrated with a sleepover party.

7. Does the pronoun agree with its antecedent?

   The cafeteria opens early; it serves breakfast beginning at 6 a.m.

   Yes No

8 – 12. Read the following summary, and use it to create a timeline of some of the events in the life of Roberto Clemente. Be sure to list events in chronological order.

In 1973 Roberto Clemente became the first Latin American player elected to the Baseball Hall of Fame. He has been called "the best right-fielder in the history of baseball." Besides winning numerous batting titles and Gold Glove awards over the years, Roberto was named the National League's MVP in 1966.

Born in Puerto Rico in 1934, Roberto started playing professional baseball with the Santurce Crabbers in 1952, just after he finished high school. Two years later, Roberto began his 18-year major league career with the Pittsburgh Pirates. He made the All-Star Team in 1960 and led the Pirates to a World Series victory that same year. The Pirates won the World Series again in 1971, and Roberto was named the Series' MVP. At the peak of his career, in September of 1972, Roberto Clemente made his 3,000th hit.

Source: HTTP://WWW.WHITEHOUSE.GOV/KIDS/DREAMTEAM/ROBERTOCLEMENTE.HTML

| Events in the Life of Roberto Clemente | |
|---|---|
| Year | Event |
| | He go to school |
| | He play Sports |
| | |
| | |
| | |
| | |
| | |
| | |

## Lesson #10

1. **A simile compares one thing to another, using the words *like* or *as*. Example:** Patty cleaned this house like a white tornado! Underline the simile.

   Jason was as fast as a jack rabbit, moving toward the finish line.

2. Choose a synonym for the underlined word.

   Great Britain is a sovereign state.

   prosperous independent sacred miniscule

3. Add the punctuation needed to make this sentence correct.

   Dora s friend is here,

4. Fill in the rest of the singular subject pronouns.

   I , She , He , Is , will

5. **All plural nouns and the pronouns *we, you,* and *they* use the verbs *are* and *were*.** Complete the sentence with a form of the verb *be* that agrees with the subject.

   You just now dismissed.

6. What is the meaning of the prefix *trans-* (transport, transfer, transit)?

   A) across, beyond, or through
   B) speak or write
   C) shape or form
   D) in a certain way

7. **Avoid using a pronoun when it makes your meaning unclear. Example:** Karla gave her mother the box, but she forgot there is no delivery today. It is unclear whether "she" refers to Karla or her mother. Rewrite the sentence so it is clear that Karla's mother forgot about the delivery.

   She gave her mother the box, but she forgot there is no deivery today.

8. Underline the pronoun; write its antecedent on the line.

The cheerleaders were exhausted and they needed a short break.

short break

9. **The simple subject is just the subject, without any modifiers. Example:** Bright red and green lights were flashing. Underline the simple subject.

Four honking geese tried to fly over the fence.

10. The root *-gram-* (telegram, diagram, grammar) is from the Greek, meaning "something spoken."

spoken written carried small

11. Underline the sentence that states a fact.

Roberto Clemente was not only a great baseball player; he was a generous and compassionate person. Roberto donated money and gave his time to create a place for underprivileged children to develop athletic skills.

12. Use the editing mark for spelling to mark two spelling errors in the following sentence.

Roberto played right feild for most of his career, and he was one of his team's most valueable hitters.

## Lesson #11

1. Choose the word that has a more positive connotation.

   The directions for this game are (complex / problematic).

2. Underline the simple subject.

   Seven bright orange pumpkins lined the shelf above the fence.

3. **Homonym Riddle:** This word names the sound a dog makes or the protective outer covering of a tree trunk. What is it?

   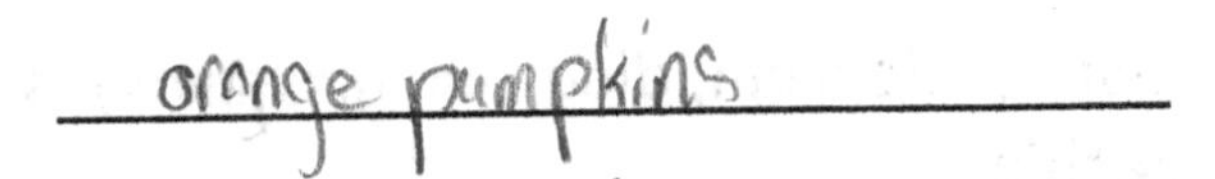

4. The subject pronouns are: I, you, he, she, it, we, you, and they. Write a subject pronoun that could replace the underlined words.

   The bridge is deteriorating. 

5. What is the meaning of the root *-dict-*? (edict, dictate, dictaphone)

   book speak between shape

6. Does the pronoun agree with its antecedent? Yes No

   I really like that café; they stay open late.

7. Choose the missing letters. ie 

   The children played pranks and got into all kinds of misch___f.

Read the next two paragraphs and use them to answer the remaining questions.

On December 23, 1972 an extremely destructive earthquake shattered the city of Managua, the capital of Nicaragua. The earthquake, which registered 6.3 on the Richter scale, toppled city buildings, destroyed people's homes, and killed thousands of Nicaraguans. Many of those who survived were injured and had lost everything. The citizens were without basic necessities, like food, safe water, electricity, and medical care. Fires blazed out of control, and communication with the rest of the world was cut off.

Roberto Clemente had often tried to help people who were disadvantaged or suffering from misfortune, and he was deeply concerned about the plight of the people of Managua. He organized some relief workers and bought supplies, which he loaded onto a small airplane called a DC-7. On New Year's Eve of 1972, Roberto and his friends attempted to fly to Managua to bring assistance to the earthquake victims. But the DC-7 crashed, and there were no survivors. Friends of Roberto Clemente were shocked and deeply saddened by the tragedy. They began to speak about their baseball hero as a great humanitarian.

Sources: HTTP://WWW.WHITEHOUSE.GOV/KIDS/DREAMTEAM/ROBERTOCLEMENTE.HTML and HTTP://NEWS.BBC.CO.UK/ONTHISDAY/HI/DATES/STORIES/DECEMBER/23/NEWSID_2540000/2540045.STM

8. What is a humanitarian?

a fan of baseball  a caring person  a great athlete  an airplane pilot

9. What is the purpose of the first paragraph?

A) to explain the life and culture of Nicaraguans during the 1970's

B) to tell a little about earthquakes

C) to give background about the disaster that led to Roberto Clemente's death

D) to explain the devastating effect of earthquakes on large cities

10. Why did Roberto attempt to fly to Nicaragua?

A) Managua was Roberto's birthplace.

B) There had been a devastating hurricane.

C) Roberto wanted to help people.

D) It was New Year's Eve

11. Which of these is a synonym for the underlined word?

plot  dilemma  event  liberation

12. Which of the following would be the best ending for the second paragraph?

A) "He was the one player that players on other teams didn't want to miss. They'd run out of the clubhouse to watch him take batting practice." - Steve Blass

B) "He was a great player. There wasn't anything he couldn't do on a baseball field." - Bill Virdon

C) "He gave his life trying to help other people. That shows you the kind of man he was." - Milo Hamilton

D) "He gave the term 'complete' a new meaning. He made the word 'superstar' seem inadequate." - Bowie Kuhn

## Lesson #12

1. What two things are being compared in this simile?

   He polished the table until it was as smooth as glass.

   ______________________ ______________________

2. List the plural subject pronouns. ________, ________, ________

3. Underline the root that has to do with "writing."

   -scrib- ➡ (scribble, scripture, transcript)

   -port- ➡ (porter, transport, portable)

   -ped- ➡ (pedal, pedestrian, biped)

   -phone- ➡ (telephone, phonograph, Dictaphone)

4. **If a plural noun ends in –s, add only the apostrophe to show possession. Example:** the boys' team **If a plural noun does not end in –s, use the apostrophe and –s to show possession. Example:** the children's room
   Add apostrophes where needed.

   The girls mothers watched the Peoples Choice Awards.

5. Add the two forms of punctuation needed to make this sentence correct.

   The buses lanes are all on the far right side of the road

6. In this sentence the pronoun and verb do not agree with the antecedent. Cross out the incorrect pronoun and verb, and write the correction on the line.

   I would love to visit Brazil since they have beautiful rainforests.

   ______________________________________

7. Use the editing mark for capitalization to mark two errors in this sentence.

   The island of Puerto rico got its name from the spanish words for "Rich Port."

8 – 12. Read the following quote by Roberto Clemente.

"Anytime you have an opportunity to make things better and you don't, then you are wasting your time on this Earth."

Think of a time when you had an opportunity to "make things better," and write a draft about your experience here.

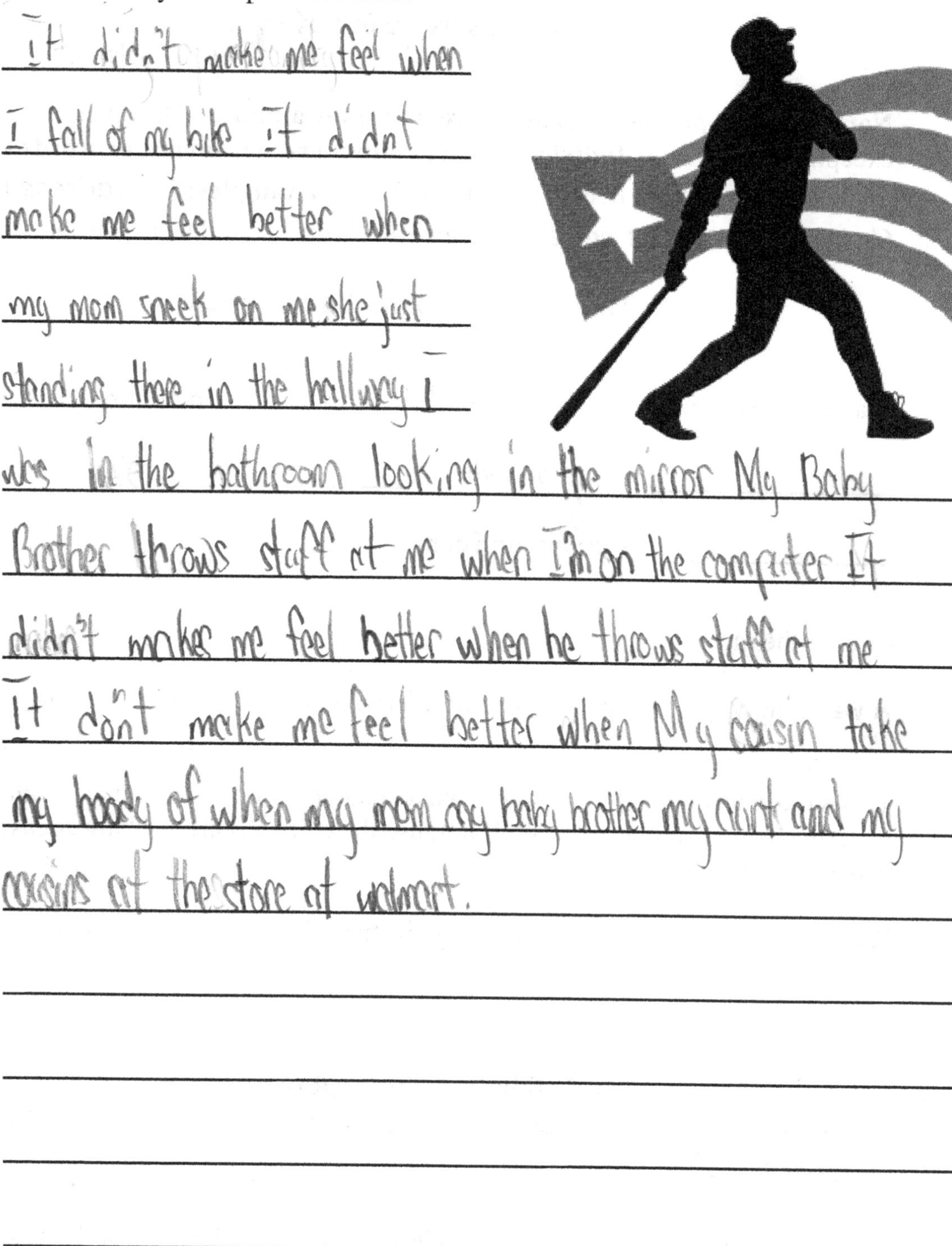

it didn't make me feel when
I fall of my bike it didnt
make me feel better when
my mom sneek on me she just
standing there in the hallway I
was in the bathroom looking in the mirror My Baby
Brother throws stuff at me when I'm on the computer It
didn't makes me feel better when he throws stuff at me
It don't make me feel better when My cousin take
my hoody of when my mom my baby brother my aunt and my
cousins at the store at walmart.

## Lesson #13

1. Underline the correct homophone.

   Are you (write / right) -handed or left-handed?

2. Underline the interjection and insert the proper punctuation after it.

   Whoops we're out of milk.

3. **Normally, an apostrophe is never used to show a plural.** However, there is an exception to this rule. **Individual letters, numbers, acronyms, or words can be made plural with the help of an apostrophe.** **Examples:** My address has two 6's in it, and my last name has three R's in it. Add an apostrophe.

   There are five YMCAs in my town.

4. Match these prefixes with their meanings. micro- morpho- male-

   ______________ ➡ bad or evil ______________ ➡ small in size

   ______________ ➡ shape or form

5. Choose the missing letters.

   A wedding v___l may be made of white lace and pearls. ie ei

6. This editing mark ( / ) tells you to make a letter lower case. Are all of the underlined words proper nouns? If not, use the editing mark for "lower case" to make corrections.

   We belong to Faith Christian Church, but there is another Church just down the street.

7. **Use a semicolon to separate things in a series if there are already commas within the items.** **Example:** The dates were June 3, 1912; February 4, 1927; and October 8, 1952. Separate the items in this sentence with semicolons.

   I have lived in Bassett, Nebraska Camden, Maine and Logan, Utah.

8. Write "action" or "being" to tell which kind of verb is used in each sentence.

A) being ➡ Norm brought some oranges from Florida.

B) action ➡ They are sweeter than most oranges.

9. Write a subject pronoun that could replace the underlined noun or nouns.

Carla and her mother will bring the salads. nouns

10. A metaphor compares two things by saying something *is* something else. **Example:** *My stomach is a grumbling ogre* that won't let me concentrate until I feed it. What two things are being compared in the example?

My stomach is a grumbling ogre that won't let me concentrate until feel it

11 – 12. This is the editing mark that tells you to add something. (∧) Rewrite the sentences below correctly.

Theodor Seuss Geisel wrote ∧ *Cat in the hat.* (The)

Theodor Seuss Geisel wrote The Cat in the hat.

He created a ~~P~~ublishing company based on the success of that famus (sp) children's book.

He created a publishing company based on the success of that famous children's book

## Lesson #14

1. **All singular nouns and the pronouns *he, she,* and *it* use the verbs *is* and *was.*** Complete the sentence with a form of the verb *be* that agrees with the subject.

   He __was______ trying to call you yesterday.

2. Add the punctuation needed to make this sentence correct.

   Remember to dot all your i s and cross all your t s

3. What is the connotation of the underlined word in this sentence?

   My dad will buy an ATV if he can get one at a decent price.

   polite straight good well-mannered

4. Find the word *tedious* in a thesaurus or dictionary. Underline its meaning.

   tiresome extremely happy ridiculous intellectual

5. Choose the missing letters.

   Use a s__a__ve to strain the cooked vegetables. ie ei

6. **Capitalize the first word and all nouns in the greeting or *salutation* part of a letter. Example:** Dear Sir: Write this salutation correctly.

   dear dr. and mrs. black __Dear Dr. and Ms. Black________

7. Separate the items in this sentence with semicolons.

   Our relatives live in Lexington, Kentucky Portland, Oregon and Denver, Colorado.

8. **A verb phrase is made up of a main verb and at least one helping (auxiliary) verb. Example:** Soledad had come to visit her brother. Underline the verb phrase in this sentence.

   They were learning the names of the constellations.

9. Write a subject pronoun that could replace the underlined noun or nouns.

It was very late when Bernard and Kyia reached the top of the mountain.

______________________

10. Is the underlined sentence a **cause** or an **effect**?

Mackenzie and Miranda are identical twins.
Hardly anyone can tell them apart.

cause effect

**Proof it!** Proofread these sentences and use editing marks to correct errors.

11. the President and his staff work in the West Wing

12. The West Wing houses the another Oval Office, the

Cabinet Room, and the roosevelt room, among others.

## Lesson #15

1. Add the punctuation needed to make this sentence correct.

   How many 7's are in your phone number

2. Underline two antonyms. prompt ordinary palatable extraordinary

3. **As you know, apostrophes are used in the spelling of contractions because certain letters are left out. Examples:** can't, they're, we'll **Apostrophes are also used to show that numbers are left out. Example:** class of '07 (2007) Add an apostrophe.

   He was born in the spring of ' 59.

4. Find these words in a thesaurus or dictionary. Underline the word that best completes the sentence.

   Mother will be loiter when she sees the broken statue!

   loiter loath livid

5. A metaphor compares two things using a form of the verb *be*. **Example:** The *fireflies were miniature torches* swirling around the meadow. What two things are being compared in the example?

   fireflies meadow

6. The prefix *thermo-* (thermometer, thermoplastic, thermostat) is from the Greek, meaning "heat."

   heat water human written

7. **If a word has only one syllable or is stressed on the last syllable, double the final consonant when adding a suffix that begins with a vowel. Example:** regret ➡ regrettable Write the word with its suffix.

   forget + -able ➡ forgetable

8. Put a ✓ next to the sentence that states an opinion.

✓ Nikola Tesla is credited with the development of the AC power system.

x Without the genius of Tesla, city streets would be dark, and subways would not have power.

9. **The pronoun *I* uses the verbs *am* and *was*.** Choose the correct verb.

I (is / are / was) an extra in the play.

10. **Capitalize the first word in the closing of a letter. Example:** Sincerely yours,
Write this closing correctly.

yours truly,

11 – 12. What words come to mind when you think of the word *friendship*? Complete the word web below with words that represent the thoughts you have about *friendship*.

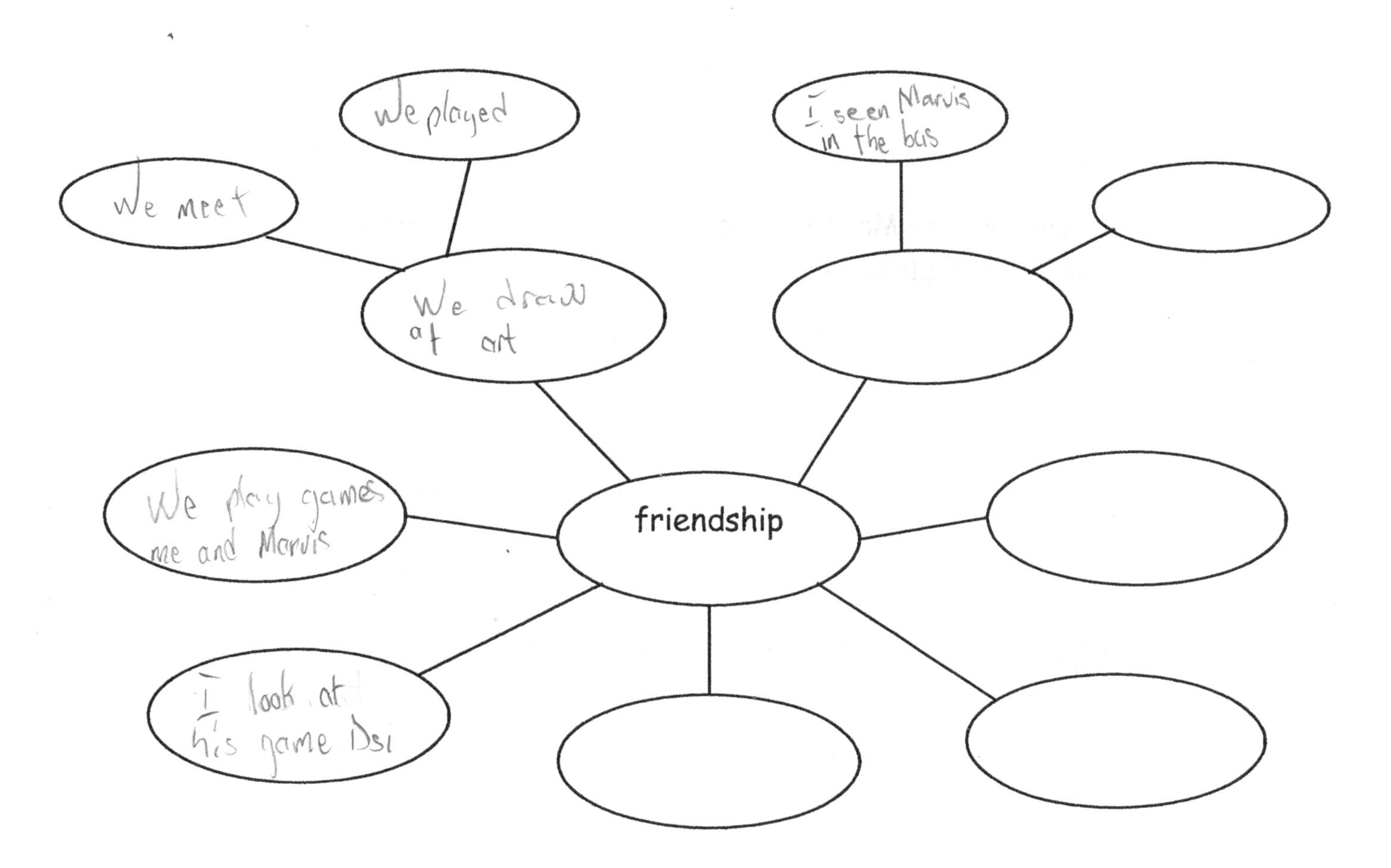

## Lesson #16

1. Add the punctuation needed to make this sentence correct.

   I ll meet you at three o'clock.

2. Find the meaning and pronunciation of the word *woe* in a dictionary. Place a ✓ next to any statement that is true.

   x Woe rhymes with go.

   ✓ A sad person is full of woe.

   ✓ Woe rhymes with shoe.

3. This is the editing mark that tells you to indent. ( ¶ ) Always indent the first line of a new paragraph. Draw the editing mark here.

   ¶

4. **Homonym Riddle:** This word means "to stumble" or "a journey." What is it? (Remember, homonyms are words that sound and are spelled the same but have different meanings.)

   A Journey

5. Separate the items in this sentence with semicolons.

   We will meet on Monday, August 7, Tuesday, September 5, and Wednesday October 4.

6. **All of the *verbs of being* can be used as helping verbs.** Write the *verbs of being* here.

   We will meet on Monday, August 7, Tuesday, September 5, and Wednesday, October 4.

7. Write a subject pronoun that could replace the underlined noun or nouns.

   Mr. Norris always assigns summer reading. Noun

8 – 12. Writing a Draft

In Senegal it is said, "When you know who his friend is, you know who he is." Do you think your friends reflect who you are? What are some things people can tell about you by getting to know your friends? Write a draft of at least five sentences.

In Senegal it is said, "When you know who his friend is, you know who he is.

## Lesson #17

1. **Use commas to separate words or phrases in a series. Example:** Frida parked the car, walked to the market, and bought fresh produce.
Insert commas in the series.

After school I usually do my homework ride my bike eat dinner and watch TV.

2. Find these words in a thesaurus or dictionary. Underline the word that best completes the sentence.

That __________ whining sound is really getting on my nerves!

winsome handsome irksome

3. **If a word ends in a vowel and single consonant, double the final consonant when adding a suffix that begins with a vowel. Example:** control ➡ controlling
Write the word with its suffix.

patrol + -ing ➡ ______________________

4. **When writing a title, capitalize the first and last word and all other important words.** Do not capitalize articles (a, an, the), conjunctions, or prepositions that have less than five letters. Write this book title correctly.

the journey to my homeland

______________________________________________

5. Underline the verb phrase in this sentence.

Marshall is finishing his homework.

6. Write a subject pronoun that could replace the underlined noun or nouns.

<u>You and I</u> will have plenty of time to go for a walk later. __________

7. **Remember, a helping verb works with a main verb; a linking verb links the subject to a word in the predicate.** Is the underlined word used as a helping verb or a linking verb?

Mr. Rodriguez <u>is</u> taking attendance. linking helping

8. Sort these nouns into two groups: common and proper.

March, town, child, lake, Trisha, country, Paris, month, Mt. Hood

common ➡ March, Trisha, Paris, Mt. Hood

proper ➡ Town, Child, Country, Lake, month

9. Complete these similes.

I feel as light as flash light.

The cat scurried through the yard like mice.

My book bag is as heavy as rock.

10 – 12. The letter below contains some capitalization errors. Use the editing marks for capitalization and lower case to mark seven errors.

Dear Mom And Dad,

This weekend we will be hosting a special event for our Parents and families. I am writing to invite you to attend our Puja, a special hindu spiritual celebration. We have been learning about the Hindu gods, Shiva and vishnu, and the goddess, Devi. Please arrive by 7:30 on Saturday evening. Don't be late – i can't wait to see you!

your loving Daughter,

Saravati

## Lesson #18

1. Insert commas in the series.

   During recess we can play basketball watch a video work on homework or play board games.

2. Use the context clues to find the meaning of *embellish* in the sentence below.

   The room is a little drab, but perhaps we can embellish it with draperies, cushions, and some fresh flowers.

   beautify     record     clean     spacious

3. Underline the interjection, and insert the proper punctuation after it.

   Look A herd of deer is grazing in our back yard.

4. Write these words with their suffixes.

   actual + -ly ➡ actually

   submit + -ing ➡ submiting

5. Underline the correct homophone; use a dictionary if you need help.

   There is plenty of (would / wood) for a campfire.

6. **A book title should always be underlined or written in italics**. Which is correct?

   The Story of My Life     *The Story of My Life*     both are correct

7. Look in the *Help Pages* for some examples of helping (auxiliary) verbs. Which of these sentences has a main verb and a helping verb? Underline it.

   I should clean my room today.     But I have plenty of time.

8. **Remember, a helping verb works with a main verb; a linking verb links the subject to a word in the predicate**. Is the underlined word used as a helping verb or a linking verb?

   Ms. Suarez was an excellent sculptor.     helping     linking

9. Circle the proper noun in each pair, and then write it correctly on the line.

monday / day ➡ Monday

mrs. hansen / teacher Mrs. Hansen

state / florida ➡ Florida

building / sears tower ➡ Sears Tower

10. **Adjectives describe nouns or pronouns; they make your writing or speech clearer and more interesting.** Underline three adjectives.

We spent seven long, hot days in Miami.

**Proof it!** The following sentences have been edited; write them correctly below.

11. The country of Panama lies between the Atlantic and Pacific oceans is a link between Central and South America

The country of Panama lie between the Atlantic and Pacific Oceans and is a link between Central and South America.

12. No wonder that Panama is called the "Crossroads Of the World!"

No wonder Panama is called the "Crossroads of the World!"

## Lesson #19

1. Marta was very <u>skinny</u> as a young girl. What is the connotation of *skinny*?

   full of skin    thin    youthful    tall

2. Choose an antonym for the underlined word.

   The investigator will <u>submit</u> her report today.

   receive    address    present    explain

3. Find the adjective *lethargic* in a thesaurus or dictionary. Underline its meaning.

   sloppy    weary    sorry    worried

4. Underline the group in which all the words are spelled correctly.

   A) engagement, strolling, relieved
   B) engagmentt, strolling, relieved
   C) engagement, stroling, relieved
   D) engagement, strolling, releived

5. Is the underlined homograph a verb or an adjective?

   Please <u>separate</u> the coins according to value.

   verb    adjective

6. Write this book title correctly.    living at the ok coral

   living at the okay coral.
   ______________________________________________

7. **A collective noun is singular; a pronoun that refers to a collective noun must agree. Example:** The <u>jury</u> has reached <u>its</u> decision.
   Choose the correct pronoun.

   The flock has lost (its / their) way.

8. Look in the *Help Pages* for some examples of helping (auxiliary) verbs. Complete the chart with six more examples of helping verbs.

Helping (Auxiliary) Verbs

| is | be | I'll | can | may |
|---|---|---|---|---|
| are | am | could | | |
| was | being | should | like | will |
| were | been | world | did | |

9. Underline the adjective that modifies the simple subject.

A hung jury is not able to agree on a verdict.

10. Underline the verb phrase; put a box around the main verb.

Phillip had been wrestling since middle school.

**Proof it!** The following sentences have been edited; write them correctly below.

11. The three states of Matter are solid, liqid, and gas.

The three states of matter are solid Liqid and gas

12. You can observe water all three states by if you freezing and boiling it.

You can observe water in all three states by freezing and boiling it.

# Lesson #20

1. What is the branch of chemistry that deals with chemical action and heat?

   biology   physics   thermochemistry   chemical engineering

2. Find the meaning of the word *accusation* in a dictionary. Place a ✓ next to the statement that is true.

   ____ The police may make an accusation.

   ____ Accusation is another word for invitation.

   ____ It is pleasant to receive an accusation.

3. **When adding a suffix that begins with a vowel, drop the final –*e*.**
   **Example:** believe + -able ➡ believable   Write the word with its suffix.

   approve + -al ➡ ______________________

4. Underline the correct homophone; use a dictionary if you need help.

   If you want to sell your bike you could put an (ad / add) in the local paper.

5. Write this film title correctly.   how I spent my summer vacation

   How I Spent My Summer Vaction

6. **A verb phrase is made up of a main verb and at least one helping (auxiliary) verb.** Add a verb phrase.

   Dawnisha __________ ______________ the piano very well.

7. Choose the pronoun that agrees with the subject.

   The team was at (their / its) best today!

8. Underline the metaphor.

   The jars of jellybeans were a rainbow of fruity sweetness, all lined up behind the counter.

9. List the *verbs of being*.

__________ __________ __________ __________

__________ __________ __________ __________

10. **Adjectives tell how many, what color, how big, how small, what kind, and so on. Use adjectives to make your writing and speech lively.** Rewrite this sentence, adding as many adjectives as you can.

The room was filled with toys and games.

________________________________________________

________________________________________________

________________________________________________

11. **Proper adjectives begin with a capital letter.** Use the editing mark for capitalization to mark the proper adjectives in this sentence.

My dog is an alaskan husky, but he gets along well with my siamese cat!

12. Complete the chart by writing an adjective in each box. The adjectives should describe the nouns listed across the top and should begin with the letter to the left. A few have been done for you.

| | ice cream | winter | football | books |
|---|---|---|---|---|
| F | | | | fascinating |
| S | strawberry | | | |
| C | | | cunning | |
| T | | | | |

## Lesson #21

1. Think about the roots of the words listed below. Underline the word that names an organism that thrives in high temperatures.

   thermophile biologist seismograph geode

2. **A run-on sentence has too many main clauses or lacks proper punctuation.** Put a ⨀ in the example to show where the first sentence should end.

   I would like to get a job this summer I'm good at landscaping, cleaning, and babysitting.

3. Write the word with its suffix.

   agitate + -ing ➡ ____________________

4. **Use commas to separate a series of adjectives if the order does not matter. Example:** The dark, tall, slender man is my father. (same meaning as tall, dark, slender man) Add commas.

   My mouth watered when I spotted some red ripe juicy watermelon.

5. A verb phrase is made up of a __________ __________ and at least one __________ __________.

6. Underline the correct pronoun.

   The committee elected Jane as (its / their) chairperson.

7. **A linking verb does not show action.** Examples of linking verbs are: appear, become, feel, seem, smell, taste, and sound. Use one of these verbs in a sentence of your own.

   ______________________________________________

   ______________________________________________

Read the following summary and use it to complete the rest of the items on this page.

## Viola Gregg Liuzzo, 1925 - 1965

Viola Liuzzo was a woman of strong moral character who believed that she had a place in the Civil Rights Movement. In Detroit, Michigan, she had been a lab technician, a wife, and the mother of five children. After seeing news reports of innocent African Americans and Whites being beaten and killed in Alabama, Viola decided she had to get involved. She left her husband, her five children, and her home to volunteer as a driver for people participating in civil rights demonstrations in the South. However, members of the Ku Klux Klan did not approve of a woman, who was both white and an outsider, shuttling marchers between Selma and Montgomery, Alabama. Less than a week after her decision to go to Alabama, Viola was dead.

Source: TEACHING TOLERANCE, A PROJECT OF THE SOUTHERN POVERTY LAW CENTER. FREE AT LAST: A HISTORY OF THE CIVIL RIGHTS MOVEMENT & THOSE WHO DIED IN THE STRUGGLE (2004).

8. What is the best way to write the underlined part of the paragraph?

   A) Selma - Montgomery, Alabama
   B) Selma & Montgomery, Ala.
   C) selma and montgomery Alabama
   D) correct as is

9. Reread the first sentence of the paragraph. Does the sentence state a fact or an opinion?

   fact opinion

10. Why did Viola go to Alabama?

   A) to get away from violence
   B) to be with her five children
   C) to participate in the Civil Rights Movement
   D) to get more information about those who had been killed

11. What can you conclude from the last two sentences of the paragraph?

   A) The Klansmen killed Viola.
   B) Viola was arrested.
   C) Viola was an African American woman.
   D) all of these

12. Which sentence could be added to support the idea that Viola "was a woman of strong moral character?"

   A) Viola was an intelligent woman, who was able to earn a post-secondary degree while raising five children.
   B) Viola worked tirelessly, spreading her enthusiasm and compassion, with little concern for her own safety.
   C) Viola was a beautiful woman, with a loving family and many friends in Detroit.
   D) Viola was haunted by news reports of beatings and murders in the South.

# Lesson #22

1. Find the word *perennial* in a thesaurus or dictionary. Underline its meaning.

   scary friendly lasting hideous

2. Underline each interjection, and insert the correct punctuation after it.

   Stop My bicycle is behind the car. Wow you almost ran over it!

3. **Capitalize the names of important documents, historic events, and time periods. Examples:** the Bill of Rights, the International Year of the Child, and the Cold War. Use the editing mark for capitalization to fix this sentence.

   This year we will learn about four parts of the geneva convention.

4. Add commas.

   The red green and white flag is Italian.

5. Fill in a pronoun that agrees with the collective noun.

   The troupe rallied behind ______________________ leader.

6. Underline the verb phrase; put a box around the main verb.

   I can stay at my cousin's house for the weekend.

7. **Linking verbs connect the subject to another part of the sentence; linking verbs do not show action. All of the *verbs of being* can be used as linking verbs. Example:** I *am* so tired! (Notice the word *tired* describes the subject, *I*.) Underline the linking verb.

   The concert was beautiful in the outdoor amphitheater.

8. **The complete predicate tells about the subject; it always includes the verb. Example:** Judy enjoys swimming. Underline the complete predicate.

   Chandra takes guitar lessons.

9. Add commas to punctuate this sentence correctly.

Martin is it true that you attended school in Tel Aviv Israel?

10. Choose the best word to show a cause-effect relationship.

The playground is covered with trash and broken glass,

(since / so / and) we won't play there.

11 – 12. **People speak in run-on sentences, but run-ons are grammatically incorrect and difficult to understand in writing.** Rewrite the example using at least three complete sentences.

**Example:** I can tell you about the time our family drove to Florida, or I can tell you about when we hiked through the Grand Canyon, and I can recall any number of special trips that I enjoyed with my parents and my sisters and brothers, even staying at home was often an adventure.

______________________________________________

______________________________________________

______________________________________________

______________________________________________

______________________________________________

______________________________________________

## Lesson #23

1. Underline two synonyms. movable palatable portable negotiable

2. ***Verbs of being* are the most common linking verbs.** Study the chart below. Say the verbs like a cheer "is – are – was – were – be – am – being – been." Repeat the cheer until you have memorized the verbs.

| *Verbs of being* | | | |
|---|---|---|---|
| is | are | was | were |
| be | am | being | been |

3. The root *–script–* or *–scrib–* comes from Latin, meaning "to write." Underline each word that refers to something written.

   prescription scribble perspire transcribe
   inscription descend scripture

4. Write the word with its suffix.

   sense + -ible ➡ ______________________

5. Look at the underlined words. If there is an error, choose the correction. If there is no error, choose "correct as is."

   Our speaker has been an ambassador to the United nations.

   A) the united nations
   B) The United nations
   C) the United Nations
   D) correct as is

6. **Helping verb + main verb = a verb phrase.** Underline the verb phrase.

   Aunt Kitty should have called by now.

7. What two things are being compared in the simile?

   Old Possum lay there on the beach all day, looking as dead as a piece of driftwood.

   ______________________ ______________________

8. Underline the complete predicate.

The costumed children waited eagerly for their turn to go onto the stage.

9. Write the eight *verbs of being* that you memorized here. Try not to look back!

__________ __________ __________ __________

__________ __________ __________ __________

10 – 12. Most people agree that habits like smoking cigarettes, riding a bike without a helmet, and consuming large quantities of sugar are unhealthy. In fact, these patterns of behavior could shorten a person's life. Make a short list of habits that you think are harmful or distasteful.

________________________________________________

________________________________________________

________________________________________________

________________________________________________

## Lesson #24

1. A task that is daunting is a little scary. A person who is dauntless is not afraid. What does the root word *daunt* mean?

   to encourage    to intimidate    to believe

2. Find these words in a thesaurus or dictionary. Underline the word that best completes the sentence.

   lumbering    strolling    gliding

   When Dylan wore all that bulky football gear, he looked funny _______ across the field.

3. Look at the underlined words. If there is an error, choose the correction. If there is no error, choose "correct as is."

   The Library of congress is the world's biggest library.

   A) library of congress    C) Library of Congress

   B) Library Of Congress    D) correct as is

4. Underline the verb phrase; put a box around the main verb.

   Terrance must have left his keys here.

5. Here are some other common linking verbs: appear become feel seem smell taste sound grow remain stay continue. Use one of these verbs in a sentence of your own.

   ______________________________________________

   ______________________________________________

6. **The complete predicate includes the verb and everything that goes with the verb (adverb, direct and indirect object, predicate nominative, predicate adjective).** Underline the complete predicate.

   Nathan knows how to bait a fishing line.

7. Draw a line through the fragment.

It was a snowy but bright winter afternoon. Around the first of December. I took my very first sled ride that day. I loved it!

8 – 12. Choose one or more of the unhealthy habits that you listed in the previous lesson. Write a short paragraph explaining why this habit should be avoided. Use adjectives to make your writing interesting; some adjectives that mean "unhealthy" are listed below.

unhealthy ➡ harmful, injurious, detrimental, caustic, damaging, toxic, destructive, hurtful, negative, adverse, unfavorable

## Lesson #25

1. **A preposition is a word that ties a noun or pronoun to other words in a sentence.** Some common prepositions are listed in the *Help Pages* in the back of this book. Find the list, and write five prepositions here.

______________________________________________

2. **A predicate adjective describes the subject; it is linked to the subject by a linking verb.** Underline the predicate adjective.

I feel sleepy.

3. Write the *verbs of being.*

________ ________ ________ ________

________ ________ ________ ________

4. **A transitive verb is an action verb which has a direct object.**

Mabel ironed the shirt.

What did Mabel do? ____________________ ➡ action verb

What did Mabel iron? ____________________ ➡ direct object

5. **The predicate always includes the verb; sometimes the predicate is just a verb and nothing else. Examples:** Everyone giggles. Sue is giggling. Next, Jason will be giggling. Underline the complete predicate.

Many children compete.

6. **If the parts of the compound subject are joined by the conjunction *and*, the verb will be plural. Example:** Shelly and Keith play violin. Fill in a verb that agrees with the subject of each sentence.

are works is run

The machine ________ beautifully. Lucy and I ________ teammates.

7. Complete the sentence with a pronoun that agrees with the collective noun.

   The company redesigned ______________________ logo.

8. **Adverbs modify (describe) verbs.** Underline the word that describes Hank's driving.

   Hank drove carefully on the slippery roads.

9. Underline the adjectives in this sentence.

   Twelve slimy snakes slithered across the sparkling floor.

10. Which part of speech should not be used very often in formal writing?

| noun | pronoun | verb | adverb |
|---|---|---|---|
| adjective | conjunction | preposition | interjection |

11 – 12. Fix this run-on by inserting a ⊙ and a ≡ to show where each sentence should begin and end.

My sister and I have always shared a bedroom she is three years older, and maybe that's why she's just a little bossy we've tried to arrange the room so that we each have the same amount of space but you see, it seems she always gets the side of the room that has a big window, so she always gets the cool breeze.

## Lesson #26

1. Which kind of verb is used in this sentence – action, linking, or helping?

   Mrs. Flora became the new Headmaster.

   action linking helping

2. **The simple predicate is the verb; it may be a single word or a few words.** Underline the simple predicate in each sentence.

   Jamie climbs the rock wall at our recreation center. The Boys Club will be climbing the cliffs at Lowing Ledges next week. The boys have climbed other hills and cliffs before.

3. **A pronoun in the predicate of a sentence may be a predicate nominative; since a predicate nominative renames the subject, it is a subject pronoun. Example:** The catcher was she. (The subject is *catcher*; the predicate nominative is *she*.) Which is correct? Underline it.

   The reporters were he and I. The reporters were him and me.

4. **Adverbs tell *how, when, where*, or *to what extent.*** Underline the adverb that tells *when*.

   We golfed yesterday.

5. **A preposition relates a noun or pronoun to another word in a sentence.** Underline the preposition.

   Donna and Roxanne walked through the museum.

6. **A direct object answers the question "what?" or "whom?" It follows a transitive (action) verb.** Underline the direct object.

   My dad assembles computers.

7. **A compound subject with two singular parts that are joined by *or* or *nor,* uses a singular verb. Example:** Paulette or Ivan usually *drives* the children to school. (Since the driver will only be one of them, the verb is singular. Paulette drives or Ivan drives.) Choose the correct verb.

Either Lageita or Doris (make / makes) brownies every Friday.

8 – 12. A tribe is like a family; it is a group of people who share common beliefs, ancestors, customs, and leaders. Although all people are born into a "tribe," there are also tribes that people choose: friends, clubs, sports teams, and church groups. Think about one of the "tribes" that you belong to, and describe it here. Write at least five sentences.

_______________________________________________

_______________________________________________

_______________________________________________

_______________________________________________

_______________________________________________

_______________________________________________

_______________________________________________

_______________________________________________

_______________________________________________

## Lesson #27

1. Underline the linking verb.

   You can see that the mountains appear closer than they really are.

2. Underline the simple predicate.

   The president approved a bill created by Congress.

3. **A complete predicate is made up of all the words in the predicate.** It may be just one word, or the complete predicate may contain several words.

   **Examples:** Engineers design.
   Engineers sometimes work with architects.

   Underline the complete predicate.

   Earl S. Tupper invented the highly useful plastic containers known as Tupperware.

4. **A predicate noun (predicate nominative) renames the subject; a predicate adjective describes the subject.** What is the predicate noun in this sentence?

   Gloria is the gardener. ______________________

5. What is the predicate adjective?

   Gloria is very clever. ______________________

6. When the pronoun is a **predicate nominative** you can reverse the words in your head to decide which pronoun is correct. Circle the correct pronoun. (Which sounds right? "He is the new pilot." or "Him is the new pilot.")

   The new pilot is (he / him).

7. Adjectives describe nouns; adverbs describe ______________________.

8. Some common prepositions are listed in the *Help Pages*. Which of these words are prepositions?

   near wonder under tomorrow against

9. **A direct object always follows an action verb; it receives the action of the verb.**
**Example:** The tutor helped Marcia. Underline the direct object.

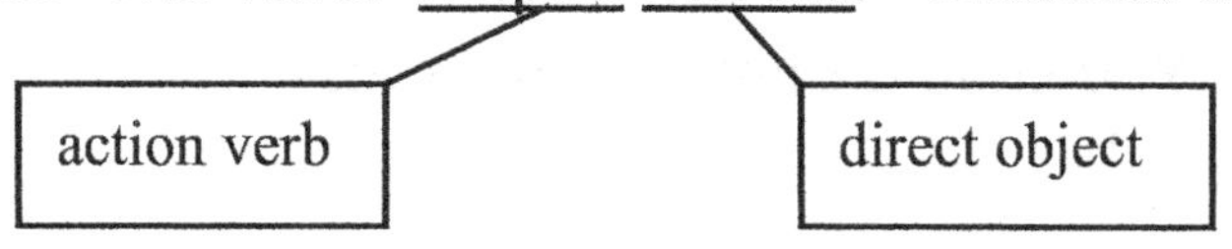


Everyone ate spaghetti.

10. **A compound subject joined by the words *or* or *nor* uses a singular verb.**
Choose the correct verb.

Neither Larson nor Aaron (run / runs) track at our school.

11. Use the editing mark for capitalization to mark two errors in this sentence.

Moiré and i did some research on siberian tigers and snow leopards.

12. Check the spelling of the words in this sentence. Use an editing mark to show any misspelled words.

The recipe says this cookie dough will yeild six dozen three-inch cookys.

## Lesson #28

1. Underline the verb phrase; put a box around the main verb.

   You should drive to the coast.

2. **Remember, the simple predicate is the verb (or verbs) only**. Underline the simple predicate.

   Congress held a heated debate about the proposed legislation.

3. **The complete predicate includes all the words in the predicate**. Underline the complete predicate.

   A physical therapist can help you with strength training.

4. Choose the pronoun that correctly completes the sentence.

   The elected officials were (she / her) and Mrs. Whiting.

5. **Adverbs can modify verbs, adjectives, or other adverbs.** Underline the adverb that tells *how*.

   Micah gently held the kitten.

6. **A prepositional phrase begins with a preposition and ends with a noun or pronoun. Example:** All the books within these walls are Tanya's. Underline the prepositional phrase.

   Shanta and Louis dance toward the back of the room.

7. Is a direct object only found in a sentence with an action verb? Yes No

8. **A compound subject is made up of two or more different subjects with the same predicate**. Underline the compound subject.

   Josh and Jeff are experts at strength training.

9. **A compound subject with two or more plural parts uses a plural verb.**
**Example:** Cats and dogs require a lot of care. Choose the correct verb.

Men and women (study / studies) art at this institute.

10 – 12. There are many ways to recycle. One way is to simply reuse containers instead of throwing them away. Even if you reuse part of a container, you are recycling. Complete the chart below with your ideas for recycling containers. A few ideas have been given.

| Item | Grocery Bags | Yogurt Container | Glass Jar | Cardboard Box |
|---|---|---|---|---|
| Idea #1 | Use plastic bags for trash; small bags are great for smaller trash cans. | | Store leftovers in refrigerator; tall thin jars are a space-saver. | |
| Idea #2 | | Fill with cut-up fruit and carry for snacks. | | |
| Idea #3 | | | | Use boxes to store items in the basement. Write content on box with marker or crayon. |

## Lesson #29

1. **Nominative case is the same as subjective case.** A predicate nominative renames the subject. Underline the subject pronoun that acts as a predicate nominative in this sentence.

   Clearly, the best players were (them / they).

2. Circle the transitive (action) verb. Underline the direct object.

   My class visited the Botanical Gardens.

3. **When the direct object is a pronoun, it must be an objective case pronoun. The objective case pronouns are: me, you, him, her, it, us, and them.** Which one of these can be either singular or plural?

   ______________________

4. **Two sentences with the same predicate can be joined to make one sentence with a compound subject. Example:** Aunt Sally can stay with us. Or, the twins can stay with us. ➡ Aunt Sally or the twins can stay with us. Join these sentences and write a single sentence with a compound subject.

   Mom can stop at the grocery. Or, Dad can stop at the grocery.

   ______________________________________________

   ______________________________________________

5. **There are three kinds of conjunctions. You already know about coordinate conjunctions: *and, or, for, but, nor, so* and *yet.* They join words, clauses, or phrases that are similar.** Complete the compound subject with a coordinate conjunction.

   Hassan ____________ Cahil will show you how to fly the kite.

6. **Adverbs often end in *-ly*.** Underline the adverb in this sentence. What verb does it modify?

   Jack waited patiently for his turn at bat. ____________________

7. Singular verbs end in *–s* (looks, acts, runs); plural verbs do not end in *–s* (see, eat, play). Choose a verb for each subject.

   the children (try / tries)   Nick (say / says)   they (think / thinks)

8. **When the parts of a compound subject are plural the verb will be plural, even when using the words *or* or *nor*. Examples:** Small shrubs or flowers *are* a nice addition to the yard. Boys and girls *study* math. Choose the correct verb.

   Pebbles or rocks (look / looks) nice next to the flower bed.

9. **The object of a preposition is a noun or pronoun that the preposition relates to the rest of the sentence. Example:** beyond the city
   (*beyond* ➡ preposition, *city* ➡ object of the preposition )
   Underline the object of the preposition in this sentence.

   The cellar is beneath the house.

Use these sentences for items 10 – 12.

Our mayor, George B. Nicely. We welcome you to Walden Hills, a diverse community where neighbors are your friends! Mayor nicely meets monthly with citazens to answer questions, listen to ideas, and gather information.

10. Underline the sentence that has no errors.

11. Draw a line through the fragment. What is missing – subject or verb?

    ____________________

12. Use two editing marks to correct the other sentence.

# Lesson #30

1. Which kind of verb is used in this sentence – action, linking, or helping?

   Noreen cut her hair every four weeks. ______________________

2. Underline the complete subject.

   One hundred shiny pennies were deposited in Tina's piggy bank.

3. Complete the sentence with a pronoun that agrees with the collective noun.

   The sixth grade class elected ____________ representatives.

4. **Use an object pronoun as a direct object or as the object of a preposition.** List the object pronouns here.

   __________ __________ __________ __________

   __________ __________ __________

5. **The noun or pronoun at the end of a prepositional phrase is the object of the preposition. Example:** The lights went out *during the storm*. (storm is the object) Underline the prepositional phrase; write the object of the preposition.

   Let's walk toward the hotel now. ______________________

6. **A prepositional phrase begins with a preposition and ends with a noun or pronoun.** Underline the prepositional phrase.

   All of the packages were wrapped and placed beneath the tree.

7. Adverbs tell how, when, where, or to what extent. Underline the adverb that tells *to what extent.*

   The boys completely destroyed that snow fort.

8. Underline the transitive verb (verb that shows action) and put a star next to the direct object.

I painted my toenails orange.

9. Two or more sentences with the same subject can be joined to make a single sentence with a **compound predicate**. **Example:** Denise writes well. Denise speaks beautifully. ➡ Denise writes well and speaks beautifully. Combine these sentences to make a single sentence with a compound verb.

Granddad picked strawberries. Granddad made a delicious pie.

______________________________________________

______________________________________________

10. **Use a conjunction to create a compound predicate. Example:** You can wait in the car. You can go for a walk. You can relax on the swing. ➡ You can wait in the car, go for a walk, *or* relax on the swing. Combine these sentences using a conjunction.

Dory collected aluminum cans. Dory took the cans to a recycling plant. Dory exchanged the cans for cash.

______________________________________________

______________________________________________

11. **A collective noun is singular; it is treated as a single unit. Collective nouns used as subjects take singular verbs. Examples:** audience claps, flock goes, jury decides, luggage arrives Choose the correct verb.

The committee (meet / meets) every month.

12. Read these two statements. Put a C next to the **cause** and an E next to the **effect**.

_____My draft had several errors.

_____Therefore, I had to spend extra time revising and editing.

## Lesson #31

1. **The subject of an imperative is "you." It is not written; it is understood.** What is the subject of this sentence?

   Please water the plants in the living room. ____________________

2. Underline the object pronoun.

   I wondered whether you got the package from them.

3. **Look for the object of the preposition at the end of a prepositional phrase.**
   **Example:** He crawled through a tunnel.
   (*through* ➡ preposition, *tunnel* ➡ object of the preposition)
   Underline the object of the preposition.

   We could see nothing beyond the horizon.

4. List three coordinate conjunctions.

   _______________ _______________ _______________

5. **Remember, a transitive verb shows action.** Underline the transitive verb.

   Howie plays the violin every afternoon.

6. A word or phrase that shows strong feeling and is able to stand alone is a(n) __________.

   A) exclamation point B) phrase C) fragment D) interjection

7. **A collective noun is singular, and takes a singular verb.** Choose the verb that agrees.

   A party of five (fit / fits) comfortably in the larger booth.

8. **When adding a suffix that begins with a consonant, do not drop the final** ***–e*****.**
   **Example:** polite + -ly ➡ politely Write the word with its suffix.

   force + -ful ➡ ________

9. Underline the metaphor.

My sister is such a princess. She never has to do dishes or sweep the floors.

10. Look in a dictionary or thesaurus and find a better word for *good*. Write your word on the line.

_______________________

11. **Capitalize the names of commercial products. Examples:** McDonald's, Sony, and Kleenex Use the editing mark for capitalization to fix this sentence.

Sharon wants a Game Boy or playstation 2 for her birthday.

12. Rewrite this sentence correctly.

My Aunt might buy me an MP3 Player for christmas.

_______________________________________________

_______________________________________________

_______________________________________________

## Lesson #32

1. Underline the verb phrase; put a box around the main verb.

   My brother was acting stubborn this morning.

2. **A prepositional phrase begins with a preposition and ends with the object of the preposition.** Underline the prepositional phrase in the following sentence; write the object of the preposition on the line.

   We stayed in the basement during the storm. ____________________

3. Underline the object pronoun.

   She and you will travel with Lisa and me.

4. **There can be more than one object in a prepositional phrase. Example:** We're supposed to share the candy <u>among Lenny, Patrice, and Greta</u>. (There are three objects.) Underline the objects of the preposition.

   The hikers moved along trails and riverbanks.

5. A transitive verb shows ________________________.

6. All of a sudden there is a <u>dearth</u> of pencils; what happened to all of them? From the context clues, you can tell that another word for *dearth* is _____.

   supply    box    shortage    sharpened

7. Choose the correct verb.

   Plants and animals (is / are) fascinating to Diana.

8. Choose the verb that agrees with the collective noun.

   A large colony of ants (live / lives) in that tree.

9. Write the word with its suffix.

sportsman + -ship ➡ ______________________________

10. Look at the word list: biology antibiotic biosphere symbiosis.
These words all contain the Greek root that means what?

written law life heat earth

11. **Capitalize professional titles** (whether or not they are abbreviated) if they are part of a name. **Examples:** Reverend Hunter or Rev. Hunter
Use the editing mark for capitalization to fix this sentence.

Mrs. Ryan is married to major Tom Ryan.

12. Check the spelling of the words in this sentence. Use the editing mark for "check spelling" to mark any words that may be misspelled.

Our new nieghbors definitly have children.

## Lesson #33

1. Underline the simple subject.

   The life of Anne Frank was brief but astonishing.

2. Which type of sentence is this?

   You can get a one-way ticket to Nashville for just $59!

   Declarative Interrogative Imperative Exclamatory

3. **Possessive pronouns show ownership; they can be singular or plural.** Sort these pronouns into two lists: singular and plural.

   my their your his our her its your

   Singular ➡ ______________________________

   Plural ➡ ______________________________

4. Fill in the object pronoun that correctly completes the sentence.

   My dad knows Sheila Wright; he works with __________ at the station.

5. **Remember, a transitive verb sends its action to a direct object.** Underline the direct object.

   Flower Clown made balloons for everyone.

6. Adverbs tell how, when, where, or to what extent. Underline the adverb that tells *when*.

   Joey is always late.

7. Fill in verbs (*was* or *were*) that agree with the subjects of these sentences.

   A swarm of bees ______________ hovering around a tree near the playground. So, the first grade class ____________ not allowed out for recess.

8. Underline the prepositional phrase in the following sentence; write the object of the preposition on the line.

   Jackson always hides behind the garage! ____________________

9. **Do not separate adjectives with commas if the order is important.**
   **Example:** The *late great* Woody Guthrie was an American folk musician.
   Which is correct?

   A) We found the next best thing.

   B) We found the, next, best, thing.

   C) We found the next, best thing.

   D) We found the next best, thing.

10. Underline the metaphor.

    There has been so much rain that my whole back yard is a swimming pool.

11. Based on what you know about the prefix *post-* and the base *-script*, what is the meaning of the word *postscript*?

    ______________________________________________________________

    ______________________________________________________________

12. Use the editing mark for capitalization to correct errors in this sentence.

    President Howard honored senator Flinton and ambassador Green.

## Lesson #34

1. **The simple subject and complete subject in a sentence may be the same.** Underline the subject.

   We read Mildred Taylor's *Roll of Thunder, Hear My Cry.*

2. Choose the correct pronoun to complete each sentence.

   The best singers I've ever heard were Terri and (him / he).

   In fact, (him / he) and Terri can dance pretty well too!

3. A transitive verb sends its action to a __________ __________.

4. Rewrite this quote with proper punctuation.

   Wow cried Lisa You hit the ball clear over the fence

   ______________________________________________

5. Choose the correct verb.

   The diner (serve /serves) all kinds of fresh pies and cakes.

6. Write the word with its suffix.

   hope + -ful ➡ ____________________

7. Which is correct?

   A) Look at that beautiful blue sky!

   B) Look at that beautiful, blue sky!

   C) Look at that beautiful blue, sky!

   D) Look at that, beautiful, blue sky!

8. Three of these words are synonyms; cross out the word that does not belong in this list.

   manuscript theater document text

9. Find the word *aghast* in a thesaurus or dictionary. Underline its meaning.

very happy deeply shocked out of breath

10. Underline the opinion.

We live in a community that is richly diverse. About fifty percent of the families are Latino, Asian, or African American.

**Proof it!** Rewrite these sentences with corrections.

11. How many of the endangered ^ species live in North America.
animal

_______________________________________________

_______________________________________________

12. However, Did you know that there are many endangered plant species in Australia?
sp

_______________________________________________

_______________________________________________

## Lesson #35

1. Draw a line between the subject and the predicate.

   Mildred was born in Mississippi.

2. Underline the object pronoun.

   You and I know how to speak to them.

3. Underline the transitive verb; write the direct object on the line.

   Jeanie mailed a letter to the President. ____________________

4. Adverbs tell how, when, where, or to what extent. Underline the adverb that tells *to what extent.*

   We completely reorganized the library.

5. **Do not separate adjectives with commas if they describe in different ways. Example:** two ripe yellow bananas (*Two* tells how many, *ripe* explains the condition, and *yellow* describes color.) Which is correct?

   A) a dozen, long, green, beans
   B) a dozen long, green, beans
   C) a dozen long green beans
   D) a dozen long, green beans

6. A person who writes is a ________.

   tempest vocalist scribe geologist

**Some possessive pronouns are used with nouns. Example:** That is my helmet.
**Other possessive pronouns can stand alone. Example:** The helmet is mine.
Choose one of these possessives to complete the next sentence:

mine yours his hers its ours theirs

7. Mine is in the house, so that must be ______________.

8 – 12. If you could invent a special dessert what would it be? Describe your dessert (what it's called, the ingredients, how and when it would be served).

___________________________________________

___________________________________________

___________________________________________

___________________________________________

___________________________________________

___________________________________________

___________________________________________

___________________________________________

___________________________________________

___________________________________________

___________________________________________

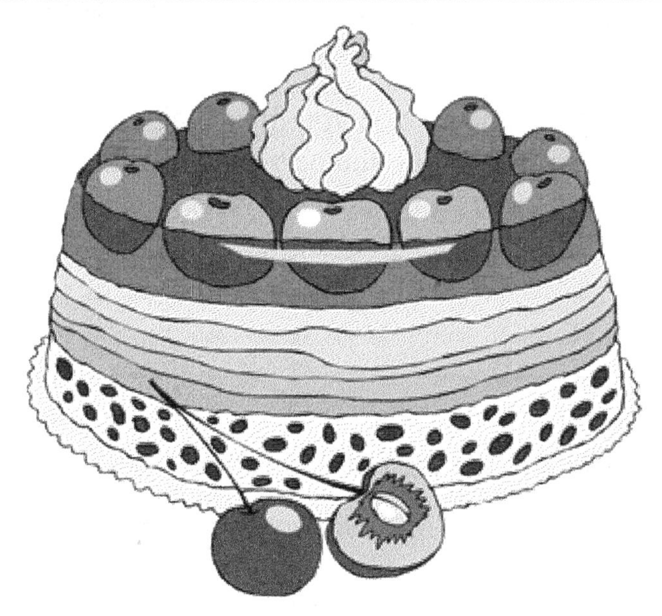

# Lesson #36

1. What is the subject of this imperative?

   Try to get the rusty nails out of this shelf. ____________________

2. Underline the predicate nominative.

   The man who was lurking around in the dark was he.

3. Beware of possessive pronouns that sound like contractions. The chart contains three examples:

| Possessive Pronouns | Contraction |
|---|---|
| its | it's ➡ it is |
| your | you're ➡ you are |
| their | they're ➡ they are |

   Choose the word that correctly completes the sentence.

   My cat likes (its / it's) bed by the window.

4. Choose a verb for each subject. bark knits growls race

   My sister ________________. The dogs ________________.

5. Are you usually reticent or are you affable? (Maybe you are both!) Circle the word that you think describes you best, and then find the meaning to see if you were right. Write the meaning of the word you chose here.

   reticent affable

   ______________________________________________________________

6. Is the homograph a verb, a noun, or an adjective?

   It looks like everyone is present today.

   verb noun adjective

7. Use what you know about roots to decide which word describes a type of clothing that keeps you warm.

antisocial thermal attractive fragmented

8. Underline the prepositional phrase in the following sentence; write the object of the preposition on the line.

The temperatures will remain high throughout the South.

______________________________

9. Look at the punctuation; which is correct?

A) our three, oldest friends
C) our three oldest friends
B) our three, oldest, friends
D) our three oldest, friends

10. Find the meaning of the word *sentinel* in a dictionary. Place a ✓ next to the statement that is true.

____ A sentinel is a part of speech.

____ A sentinel is a guard.

____ A sentinel is a special breed of dogs.

11. Is this statement a fact or an opinion?

Lawrence Wilder will be a guest speaker at this month's meeting of the Legacy Group.

fact opinion

12. What is wrong with this sentence?

Shasta and Lenny, the two very best guitarists around!

______________________________________________

______________________________________________

## Lesson #37

1. **An intransitive verb is an action verb that has no direct object.** Nothing is receiving the action of the verb. **Examples:** Jordan *plays soccer.* (*plays* ➡ transitive verb; *soccer* ➡ direct object) Jordan plays very well. (*What does Jordan play? There is no direct object.*) Underline the sentence that has an intransitive verb.

   Eugenia studies piano at the Music Settlement. She practices every day.

2. **An indefinite pronoun must agree with other pronouns in a sentence. These indefinite pronouns are singular and must be paired with other singular pronouns.**

| | | | | |
|---|---|---|---|---|
| another | each | everything | nobody | other |
| anybody | either | little | no one | somebody |
| anyone | everybody | much | nothing | someone |
| anything | everyone | neither | one | something |

**Example:** There is no waiting, so anybody can take his turn now. Choose the possessive pronoun that agrees with the singular indefinite pronoun.

Everyone needs to bring (her / their) dancing shoes tomorrow.

3. Match these subjects with their verbs.

| | |
|---|---|
| I | were |
| He | am |
| You | was |

4. Choose the correct subject pronouns to complete the sentence.

   (He / Him) and Marnie will clean, so Jason and (I / me) can finish the painting.

5. Choose the correct homophones.

   No one is (aloud / allowed) to (by / buy) a yearbook unless it has been preordered.

6. Write the plural of each noun. woman ➡ ______________________

   goose ➡ ________________ snowman ➡ ____________________

7. **When a word ends in a consonant plus *y*, change the *y* to *i* before adding most suffixes. Example:** angry + -ly ➡ angrily Write the word with its suffix.

carry + -er ➡ ______________________

Read the paragraphs, and use the information to complete the following items.

Helen Keller was born a healthy child in Tuscumbia, Alabama in 1880. But when Helen was just nineteen months old she became very sick. No one knows for sure what caused the illness, but her parents were <u>ecstatic</u> when they saw that Helen would survive the ordeal. Shortly afterward, Helen's mother realized that the child's sickness had left Helen both deaf and blind. As Helen grew, her parents understood that they would need special help in order to teach her anything at all. Helen needed to learn basic table manners, how to care for herself, and most of all, how to communicate with her beloved mother and father.

The Kellers sought advice from a famous inventor, Alexander Graham Bell. Dr. Bell believed that all children - including deaf and blind children - could learn. He suggested that the Kellers contact the director of the Perkins Institute, a school for deaf and blind children. Michael Anagnos happily recommended a graduate of the Institute, Anne Sullivan. Ms. Sullivan became Helen's teacher and lifelong companion. Later, Helen herself would become a famous teacher and author.

Source: Royal National Institute of the Blind; Content author: corpinfo@rnib.org.uk

8. Who was Michael Anagnos?

A) a famous inventor
B) Helen Keller's teacher
C) director of the Perkins Institute
D) a doctor for deaf and blind children

9. Why did Helen's parents contact Dr. Bell?

A) Dr. Bell believed that all children could learn.
B) Dr. Bell was knowledgable about children with disabilites.
C) They needed help.
D) all of these

10. Helen's parents were <u>ecstatic</u> when they saw that Helen would survive.
What is the meaning of *ecstatic*?

A) overjoyed B) frightened C) disappointed D) enraged

11. Reread the sentences in the second paragraph. Is the information given based mostly on fact or opinion? fact opinion

12. Use a conjunction to join these sentences. Write the compound sentence.
Helen Keller was born on June 27, 1880. She died on June 1, 1968.

______________________________________________

## Lesson #38

1. **An intransitive verb is an action verb, but it has no direct object.** Put a ✓ next to the sentence that has an intransitive verb.

    ____ In the year 1900, the Boxer Rebellion began in China.

    ____ Armed forces attacked the foreign embassy in the city of Beijing.

2. **These indefinite pronouns are plural and must be paired with other plural pronouns.**

    both few many others several

    **Example:** Others will be showing their artwork at the fair.
    Choose the possessive pronoun that agrees with the plural indefinite pronoun.

    Many of the band members bring (his / their) own water bottles.

3. Underline the collective noun; choose the verb that agrees.

    Nela was astonished to find that a litter of kittens (were /was) the cause of all that noise.

4. Should you use the pronoun *I* or the pronoun *me*? **Remember, *I* ➡ subject; *me* ➡ object.** Choose the correct pronoun for this sentence.

    Come and play football with Terrence and (I / me).

5. Underline the prepositional phrase in the following sentence; write the object of the preposition on the line.

    We were so distracted; we walked right past the theater entrance!

    ______________________

6. Which two are synonyms? drenched hungry thirsty parched

7. Underline the verb phrase; put a star next to the main verb.

    Maureen does live here.

Use the information below and the paragraphs in the previous lesson (as well as anything you know about Helen Keller) to complete the graphic organizer.

Laura Bridgman was the first blind and deaf child to receive a formal education at the Perkins Institute. Laura was born in December of 1829, fifty years before Helen Keller. Like Helen, Laura became very sick as a baby, and the illness left her blind and deaf. She also had a much-loved teacher, Dr. Samuel Howe, who established the Perkins Institute and devoted his life to educating blind and deaf students.

Laura was very famous in the 1800's. People from all over would come to watch her do many of the things that sighted and hearing children could do. People were amazed because Laura was incredibly bright; she communicated easily through finger-spelling. People observed as Laura studied geography, learned to sew, and asked questions endlessly. These visits helped to change the public's attitudes about blind and deaf people. Once, Laura was visited by a famous writer from England, Charles Dickens. Dickens wrote about Laura in a book called American Notes, and that is how Helen Keller's parents first heard about Laura Bridgman.

Laura spent most of her life at the Perkins Institute. As an adult, she worked at the school and even became a very demanding teacher. One of Laura's students was Anne Sullivan, who later became the teacher of Helen Keller. Laura Bridgman died in 1889.

Source: McGinnity, B.L., Seymour-Ford, J. and Andries, K.J. (2004) Laura Bridgman. Perkins History Museum, Perkins School for the Blind, Watertown, MA

8 – 12. Fill in words and short phrases to complete the comparison chart.

| Laura Bridgman | Both | Helen Keller |
|---|---|---|
| | | |

## Lesson #39

1. Does an action verb always have a direct object? Yes No

2. **These indefinite pronouns can be either singular or plural**; it depends on how they are used in the sentence.

   all any more most none some

   **Examples:** <u>More</u> of the magazine is printed in color now, so <u>it</u> is very popular. (*More* refers to the singular *magazine.*) <u>More</u> of the volcanoes are active, so they can erupt at any time. (*More* refers to the plural *volcanoes.*) Decide whether the indefinite pronoun is singular or plural, and choose the other pronoun that agrees.

   <u>Some</u> of the club members have already paid (her / their) fees.

3. Fill in verbs that agree with the subjects of these sentences.

   is are was were

   Nigeria, Ethiopia, and Egypt ______________ in Africa. Neither

   Pakistan nor India ________________ part of Africa.

4. Choose the word that correctly completes the sentence.

   That baseball glove is (mine / mines); yours is over there!

5. What are two things being compared in the simile?

   "Love is like a beautiful flower which I may not touch, but whose fragrance makes the garden a place of delight just the same." - Helen Keller

   ________________________________________________

6. Map makers sometimes begin with an <u>aerial</u> photograph of a city. What is an *aerial* photo?

   A) a close-up view
   B) a black and white print
   C) a bird's eye view
   D) an atlas

7. **A clause is independent if it has its own subject and verb; an independent clause can stand on its own.**

**Examples:** I grew up in Youngstown, and I went to Ursuline High School.
clause one clause two

Underline each independent clause.

The car was unlocked, but the keys weren't in it.

8. Find the meaning of the word *latent* in a dictionary. Place a ✓ next to the statement that is true.

____ Latent means hidden.

____ Latent is a man-made material.

____ Latent means "always late."

9. **Do not capitalize professional titles if they are not part of a person's name.**
**Example:** Darlene's dentist is *Doctor* Vann, but she saw another *doctor* last week. Which is correct?

Senator Montgomery the Senator from Utah

10. Which is correct?

Cardinal Kerrigan the cardinal from Washington both are correct

11. Which type of sentence is this?

You should read *Let the Circle Be Unbroken.*

Declarative Interrogative Imperative Exclamatory

12. What is the subject of the following sentence?

Please cancel my appointment for Friday. ____________________

## Lesson #40

1. **A linking verb does not show action; a linking verb never has a direct object. All the forms of *be* can be used as linking verbs.** Put a ✓ next to the sentence with a linking verb.

   ____ The writings of Anne Frank are inspiring.

   ____ We read her book in school.

2. Decide whether the indefinite pronoun is singular or plural, and choose the other pronoun that agrees.

   All of the ice cream (are / is) vanilla.

3. **Use a comma to separate two independent clauses joined by a conjunction; place the comma after the first clause before the conjunction. Example:** The attorney filed his report, but the trial was pending. Insert a comma.

   The jury was selected and the witnesses were sworn in.

4. Underline the object pronoun.

   They all stood and applauded us.

5. These sentences have the same subject. Use a conjunction to join the sentences; make a single sentence with a compound predicate.

   Somebody unlocked the gate. Somebody left the gate open.

   ______________________________________________

   ______________________________________________

6. Sometimes the difference between a fact and an opinion is just a few words. Write F if it is a fact; write O if it is an opinion.

   ____ Helen Keller often gave Anne Sullivan credit for opening up the world to her.

   ____ Anne Sullivan was truly a miracle worker.

7. What is the connotation of the underlined word in this sentence?

Everyone knows that smoking cigarettes is just not <u>cool</u> anymore.

fresh cold fashionable chilly

8 – 12. Here are two quotes. Choose one and write about what the quote means to you. Write a paragraph of at least five sentences.

Keep on beginning and failing. Each time you fail, start all over again, and you will grow stronger until you have accomplished a purpose - not the one you began with perhaps, but one you'll be glad to remember.

- Anne Sullivan

Life is either a great adventure or nothing. - Helen Keller

______________________________________________

______________________________________________

______________________________________________

______________________________________________

______________________________________________

_______________________

_______________________

_______________________

_______________________

_______________________

## Lesson #41

1. Look at this sentence: The berries grow ripe. The verb does not show action but links the subject to its condition.

   What is the subject? ______________________________

   What is the subject's condition? ______________________

2. **A relative pronoun relates a dependent clause to the rest of the sentence.** The relative pronouns are: that, which, who, whom, and whose.
   **Example:** The color <u>that I chose</u> was also Maureen's favorite.
   Underline the relative pronoun and dependent clause in this sentence.

   The bell that rings at noon signals the beginning of the lunch hour.

3. **A prepositional phrase may come between a subject and its verb; be sure the verb agrees with the subject. Example:** The <u>substance</u> *between the walls* <u>is</u> insulation. (The subject and verb are underlined.) Choose the verb that agrees.

   The flowers along the fence (is / are) dahlias.

4. **An analogy is a comparison between two things.** To complete a word analogy, you must determine the relationship between the first two words.

   *Flower* is to *garden* as ______________ is to *forest*.

   Which is true of the relationship between the first two words?

   A) flower is the opposite of garden
   B) flower and garden are synonyms
   C) flower is part of a garden
   D) flower is a type of garden

5. Which word correctly completes the analogy?

   *Flower* is to *garden* as ______________ is to *forest*.

   daffodil deciduous tree azalea

6. Choose the word that correctly completes the sentence.

   Jeremy finished (he / his) homework at school.

7. Which sentence is punctuated correctly?

A) The torch was lit, and the ceremonies began.

B) The torch was lit and, the ceremonies began.

C) The torch was lit and the ceremonies began.

D) The torch, was lit and the ceremonies, began.

**Many adjectives can be converted to adverbs by adding *–ly*.** Study the chart.

| Adjective | Example | Adverb | Example |
|---|---|---|---|
| slow | a slow train | slowly | moved slowly |
| immediate | immediate action | immediately | call immediately |
| final | my final decision | finally | finally arrived |

8. Underline the adverb in this sentence; circle the adjective.

The house is messy, but we can quickly tidy it up.

9. Combine these three sentences to make one sentence with a compound predicate.

Markus cleared the table. Markus washed the dishes. Markus swept the floor.

______________________________________________

______________________________________________

10. Are the underlined words synonyms or antonyms? synonyms antonyms

The <u>substandard</u> living conditions created a <u>perfect</u> recipe for disaster.

11. Fill in *verbs of being* that agree with the compound subjects of these sentences.

Drought and famine __________ common problems facing the people of Ethiopia.

Ethiopia and other African countries ___________ developing ways to cope with these ongoing crises.

12. **Capitalize club titles** such as Ski Club, Boy Scouts, and National Honor Society. Use an editing mark to indicate the word that should be capitalized.

Dwayne hopes to become a member of mensa.

## Lesson #42

1. **A linking verb links the subject with something in the predicate: a word that describes or renames the subject. With a linking verb, there is no direct object.** Which sentence uses a linking verb?

   A) The camp counselor was funny. B) He read our names with an accent.

2. **What is a dependent clause?** Look at this **example:** The flowers which I planted in the spring never bloomed. [If the dependent clause is removed, the sentence still makes sense: The flowers never bloomed. But the dependent clause (which I planted in the spring) cannot stand alone.]
   Underline the dependent clause in the following sentence.

   The guests who stayed at my house just loved the view from the front porch.

3. Choose the verb that agrees.

   The dishes in the kitchen sink (was / were) rinsed already.

4. **Do not capitalize titles that are not part of someone's name. Example:** Professor Harvey and another professor will teach the course.
   Which is correct?

   Governor James    governor of Kansas    both    neither

5. Convert each adjective to an adverb by adding *–ly*.

   polite ➡ ____________ quick ➡ ____________ new ➡ ____________

6. **A clause is any group of words with its own subject and verb; clauses are usually part of a sentence. Example:** I sat in the swing even though it was too small. I didn't break it because I am not very heavy.
   Underline the three clauses in the following sentence.

   When I am late, Esther puts dinner in the oven, and she sets the table.

7. Underline the complete predicate.

   Monopoly is one of my favorite board games.

8. This sentence states an opinion. Change it a little to make it a fact; write the fact below.

The eruption of Mount Vesuvius in 79 A.D. was the most devastating event imaginable at the time.

______________________________________________

______________________________________________

9. Underline the complete subject.

Paper money, quirky little markers, and those plastic houses make the game really interesting!

**Be sure to use the correct forms of *be* with subject pronouns.** See below.

| Number | Subject Pronoun | Present | Past | Examples |
|---|---|---|---|---|
| Singular | I | am | was | I am late. I was stuck. |
| Singular | he, she, it | is | was | He is here. It was my turn. |
| Plural | we, you, they | are | were | We are happy. You were next. |
| Plural | he and she; you and I; they and we, etc. | are | were | He and I are friends. They and we were neighbors. |

10 – 12. Write three sentences of your own, using subject pronouns and forms of the verb *be*.

______________________________________________

______________________________________________

______________________________________________

______________________________________________

______________________________________________

## Lesson #43

1. Look at the verb in each sentence. Write A for "action" or B for "being" to tell how the verb is used in each sentence.

   ____ Dolores sang in a girl's band. ____ She was the lead singer for two years.

2. **A relative pronoun must refer to an antecedent. Example:** The girl <u>who</u> you saw was my sister. The relative pronoun (who) relates to *girl*. Circle the antecedent in this sentence.

   Many children <u>whose</u> parents are immigrants speak multiple languages.

3. List the object (objective case) pronouns.

   __________ __________ __________ __________

   __________ __________ __________

4. **Remember, the verb must agree with the subject, regardless of a prepositional phrase that may come between the subject and verb. Example:** My parents' <u>anniversary</u>, along with Fabian's birthday, <u>makes</u> for a very busy weekend. Underline the simple subject and verb in this sentence.

   The nominees, along with their guests, walk on the red carpet.

5. *Music* is to *jazz* as *insect* is to ______________.

   spider rock species harmony

6. Which is a **cause** and which is an **effect**? Write C or E.

   _____As a result of the new traffic patterns, _____there were fewer accidents at the intersection.

7. Choose the best word to show a cause-effect relationship.

   I didn't answer the phone, (therefore / so / because) I didn't hear it ringing.

8. **Adverbs that tell *how* often end in *–ly*.** Choose one of the adverbs in the list and use it in a sentence of your own.

<u>Adverbs That Tell *How*</u>

quickly loudly slowly perfectly eagerly happily
angrily calmly willingly gracefully greedily noisily
quietly wildly politely unbelievably selfishly sadly
kindly softly

________________________________________________________

9. **An independent clause has its own subject and verb and can stand alone as a sentence by itself.** Underline two independent clauses in this sentence.

My dress is pink, and my sandals are white.

10. Fill in *verbs of being* that agree with the subjects of these sentences.

Isadora and Amelia ________ in the same class this year. Isaac and Kendall _____________ in that class last year.

11. Use the editing marks for capitalization and lower case to correct errors in this sentence.

The Pastor of our Church is reverend Wilson.

12. What does a declarative sentence do?

tells something
asks something
gives a command
shows strong feeling

## Lesson #44

1. Circle the verb; underline the direct object.

   Marla creates delicious pastries in her new kitchen.

2. Underline the relative pronoun and dependent clause in this sentence.

   Mr. Lawson who was my third grade teacher is now the principal.

3. Choose the verb that agrees.

   The President, with bodyguards, (arrive / arrives) at noon today.

4. *Buy* is to *bought* as *draw* is to _________.

   dragged    drought    drew    delivered

5. Underline the adverb in this sentence.

   Mrs. Whitmore frequently changes our seating arrangement.

6. **A compound sentence is made up of two or more independent clauses.** Underline the two independent clauses in this compound sentence.

   I'm going to the library, and I have to pick up my brother at his school.

7. Choose the possessive pronoun that correctly completes the sentence.

   (Your / Mine) telephone number is on the invitation.

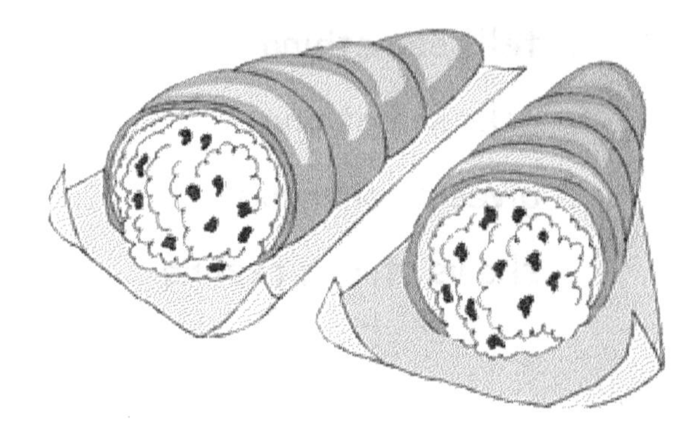

Read this information about the *quagga*, and then complete the items on this page.

Have you ever seen a quagga? Probably not. The quagga is a type of zebra, and it became extinct in 1883 when the last one died at a zoo in Amsterdam you see, the quagga looked so much like a zebra that a lot of people didn't notice the difference since the quagga had zebra-like stripes, but really it was only striped near the front of its body and it was solid brown from its midsection to its tail.

Equus quagga

8. Underline the sentence that has no errors.

9. Draw a line through the fragment.

10 – 12. One of the sentences is a run-on. Rewrite it below. Add or take out words as needed, and use proper punctuation, capitalization, and conjunctions to make sentences that work.

______________________________________________

______________________________________________

______________________________________________

______________________________________________

______________________________________________

______________________________________________

______________________________________________

______________________________________________

______________________________________________

## Lesson #45

1. Circle the verb in this sentence.

   The month of December always seems so short!

2. What kind of verb did you circle in the item above?

   action    linking    helping

3. The interrogative pronouns are: **what, which, who, whom,** and **whose.** Choose the correct pronoun.

   (What / Which) is the title of the story?

4. **An analogy is a comparison between two things**. Look at the following word analogy. cake : dessert :: soda : beverage (It reads "*Cake* is to *dessert* as *soda* is to *beverage.*") What is the relationship between *cake* and *dessert*?

   ______________________________________________

5. A compound sentence is made up of at least two i________________

   c________________.

6. Fill in the object pronoun that correctly completes the sentence.

   I know a lot about Ben Franklin; we read about ______________ in our history class.

7. Choose the correct verb.

   Both *Le Gourmet* and *Self Portrait* (were / was) among the paintings in Picasso's "Blue Period."

8. Rewrite this opinion as a fact.

   Electricity revolutionized the lives of Americans in the twentieth century.

   ______________________________________________

   ______________________________________________

Read the next two paragraphs before completing the rest of the items on this page.

In 1992, Rigoberta Menchú became the youngest person ever to receive the Nobel Peace Prize. She was just 23 years old. Rigoberta was born in the highlands of Guatemala during a time when her people, the Quiché (pronounced kēchā'), were persecuted by the wealthy and powerful landowners of Guatemala. Rigoberta grew up very poor. She and her family supported their meager way of life by picking cotton and coffee on the plantations of the rich. The Menchú family also planted corn and beans, which they harvested to feed themselves. Life was so harsh that Rigoberta's younger brother died of malnutrition. Worst of all, most of the Menchú family members were killed, because they dared to organize against the political powers in Guatemala.

But Rigoberta escaped, and despite the danger, she continued to tell the world about the poverty and <u>destitution</u> of her people. She wrote a book entitled *I, Rigoberta Menchú*, which explained everything. When people read the book, they were outraged, and Rigoberta received death threats. This made it impossible for Rigoberta to continue living in her homeland. She was exiled to Mexico and other parts of the world, where she continued to fight for the rights of women and indigenous peoples.

Source: *LES PRIX NOBEL. THE NOBEL PRIZES 1992*, EDITOR TORE FRÄNGSMYR, [NOBEL FOUNDATION], STOCKHOLM, 1993.

9. Reread the first sentence of the first paragraph. Does it state a fact or an opinion?

   fact     opinion

10. What was the effect of the publication of Rigoberta's book?

   A) People were outraged.
   B) Rigoberta had to go into exile.
   C) Rigoberta received death threats.
   D) all of these

11. Which of the following is a synonym for the underlined word?

   hardship     notoriety     culture     politics

12. What is the purpose of the two paragraphs?

   A) to tell about the life of a Nobel Peace Prize winner
   B) to endorse a book called *I, Rigoberta Menchú*
   C) to explain the culture and history of the Quiché
   D) all of these

## Lesson #46

1. Put a ✓ next to the sentence with a linking verb.

   ____ Rigoberta's story upset a lot of people.

   ____ She became a symbol of her people's will and determination.

2. **The interrogative pronoun *who* is used as a subject or a predicate nominative; it corresponds with the pronouns: *he*, *she*, or *they*.** Who is your teacher? (Think: She is your teacher.) Choose the correct pronoun.

   (Who / Whom) is coming to your graduation ceremony?

3. Which word correctly completes the analogy?

   grilled cheese : sandwich :: cherry : ________

   pie hamburger dessert cocoa

4. **A compound sentence has two or more independent clauses joined by a conjunction (and, but, or).** Underline the two independent clauses in this sentence.

   My rollerblades are too tight for me, but you can use them if they fit you.

5. Which is a **cause** and which is an **effect**? Write C or E.

   _____We brought rain gear to the outdoor concert, _____ since the weather forecast called for light showers.

Read the following quote by Rigoberta Menchú, and answer the questions that follow.

"The earth is the root and the source of our culture. She keeps our memories, she receives our ancestors and she therefore demands that we honor her and return to her, with tenderness and respect, the good that she gives us. We have to take care of her and look after mother earth so that our children and grandchildren may continue to benefit from her. If the world does not learn now to show respect to nature, what kind of future will the new generations have?"

- RIGOBERTA MENCHÚ

6. Rigoberta Menchú compares the earth to what?

   the ancestors   our mother   her grandchildren   our memories

7. Based on the quote, you can assume that Rigoberta Menchú would support which of the following?

   A) educating children about conservation

   B) legislation aimed at preserving the environment

   C) celebrations like Earth Day

   D) all of these

8 – 12. Rigoberta says we should "honor [the earth] and return to her, with tenderness and respect, the good that she gives us." What do you think she means? Write your thoughts below.

______________________________________________

______________________________________________

______________________________________________

______________________________________________

______________________________________________

______________________________________________

## Lesson #47

1. **The interrogative pronoun *whom* is used as a direct object or object of a preposition; it corresponds with the pronouns: him, her, or them.** To whom did you give the box? (Think: I gave the box to him.) Choose the correct pronoun.

   To (who / whom) did you make the call?

2. **An analogy is a comparison between two things.** Look at the following word analogy. hot : cold :: sweet : ________
   What is the relationship between the first two words?

   synonyms antonyms homonyms categories

3. Combine these two sentences to make a compound sentence. Write a new sentence using a conjunction (and, or, but).

   We're allowed to go to the park. We have to call home before 4:00 p.m.

   ______________________________________________

   ______________________________________________

4. Underline the correct possessive pronoun.

   (Your / Mine) is the blue one.

5. Underline the verbs that agree with the subjects of these sentences.
   Tiger Woods and other professional golfers (compete / competes) in The Masters Tournament. Jack Nicklaus and Arnold Palmer (was / were) great competitors in The Masters.

6. Write an F if the statement is a fact; write O if it is an opinion.

   _____ According to the National Weather Service, yesterday's high temperature was a sweltering 98°!

7. Theresa was hard-working and successful; she was very ambitious.
   Which word could replace the underlined word without changing the meaning of the sentences?

   pushy ruthless motivated

8. Some words can be used as either adverbs or prepositions. **Adverbs modify verbs; prepositions are found at the beginning of a prepositional phrase. Examples:** I have visited the museum before. (adverb tells when) There is calm before a storm. (begins a prepositional phrase) What part of speech are these words?

above down near beside under off

A) adverbs B) prepositions C) It depends on how the word is used in a sentence.

9. Choose the correct pronoun.

You teachers give (us / we) kids too many directions!

10 – 12. You can use the graphic organizer below for brainstorming. First, choose a topic, and write it in the middle. Then, complete the wheel by filling in adjectives that describe your topic.

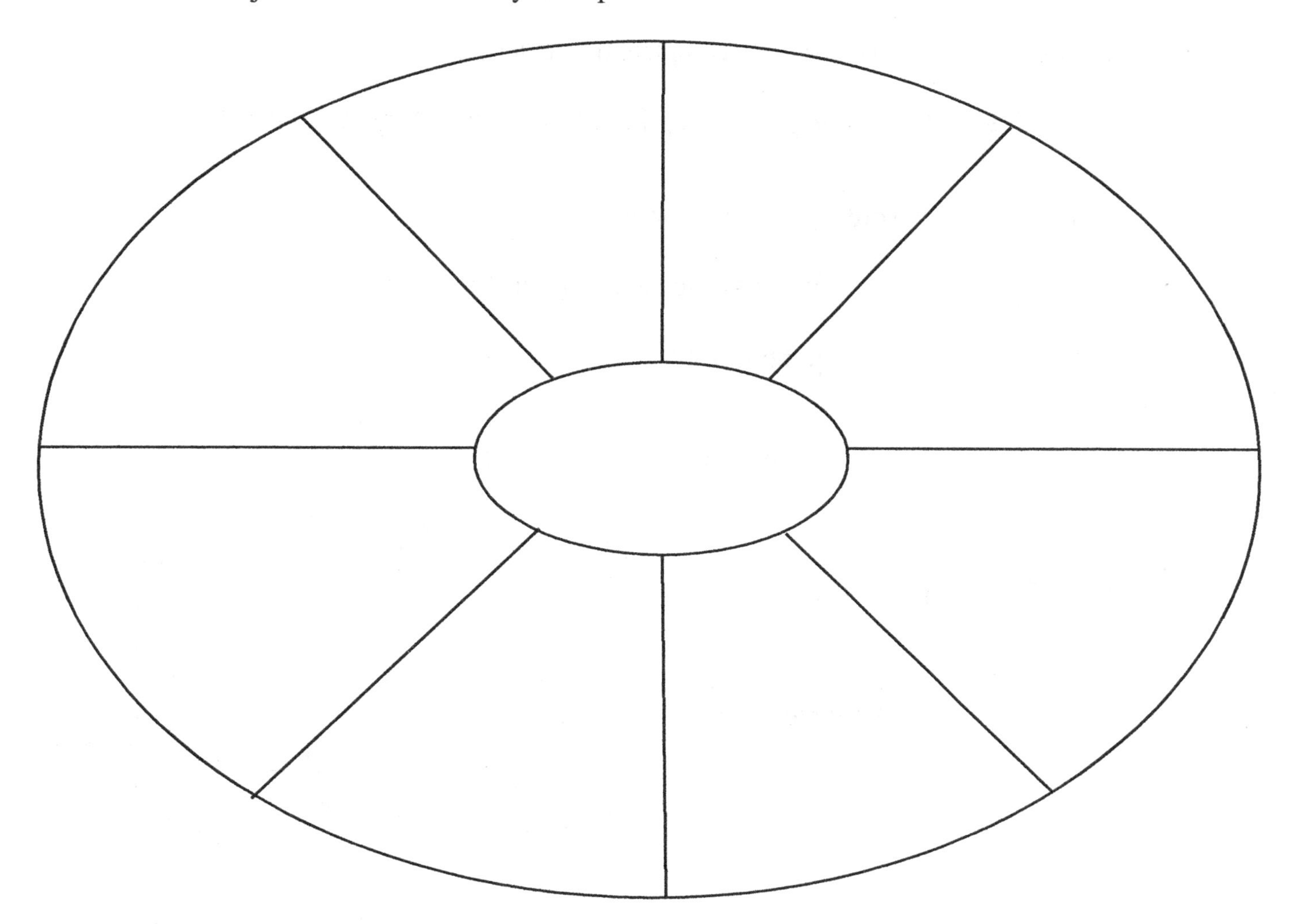

## Lesson #48

1. **The pronoun *whom* – like *him* and *them* – is used as a direct object or as the object of a preposition**. When used as an object, each ends in *m* (*whom, him,* and *them*). Choose the correct pronoun.

   With (who / whom) will you be riding?

2. Choose the word which will complete the analogy. hot : cold :: sweet : ______

   sugary    bitter    scalding    chilly

3. **The verb in a sentence must agree with its subject (nominative case) pronoun.** Match these singular and plural subject pronouns with the correct form of *walk*.

   He ____________________.    They ____________________.

   We ____________________.    It ____________________.

4. Choose the words that correctly complete the sentence.

   (Its / It's) raining and they forgot (their / they're) umbrellas!

5. Is the underlined word a preposition or an adverb?

   The restrooms are <u>near</u> the exit.

   preposition    adverb

6. Match these subjects with their verbs.    (are / is)

   Did you know there ____________ a new litter of pigs in the barn?

   The piglets ____________ never far from their mother.

7. Which word correctly completes the analogy? teach : teacher :: steal : _____

rob thief learn corrupt

8. Look at the underlined words. If there is an error, choose the correction. If there is no error, choose "correct as is."

Rigoberta Menchú was born on January 9, 1959.

A) January 9 1959.
C) Jan. 9, 1959
B) january 9, 1959.
D) correct as is

9. Circle a pair of correlative conjunctions which will correctly complete the sentence.

either/or neither/nor both/and whether/or

The weather was so disappointing during our vacation; we had _______ sunshine, _______ warm temperatures while we were at the beach.

10. **You can use a semicolon to separate two independent clauses without a conjunction.**

**Example:** The physician's assistant checked Ryan's blood pressure; it was within the normal range. (The semicolon takes the place of the conjunction.)

Insert a semicolon.

Many buses were late today the roads were very icy.

11. Underline the sentence that states a fact.

The Walden Hills School District is immense, yet organized. The district maintains six elementary schools and two high schools.

12. Choose the correct verb.

Phillip and his mom (play / plays) a beautiful duet on the piano.

## Lesson #49

1. **Verbs have four principal parts: present, past, present participle, and past participle.** Study the examples in the chart and fill in the empty spaces.

| Principal Parts of Regular Verbs | | | |
|---|---|---|---|
| Present | Past | Present Participle | Past Participle |
| look | looked | looking | has looked |
| open | opened | opening | has opened |
| dry | A) | drying | B) |
| C) | waited | D) | has waited |

2. **A demonstrative pronoun points out a particular person, place, or thing**. The demonstrative pronouns are: **this, that, these,** and **those**.
**Example:** I put <u>those</u> on the shelf, because they are not for sale.
Use one of the demonstrative pronouns in a sentence of your own.

______________________________________________

______________________________________________

3. Choose the homophone that makes each sentence correct. Use a dictionary if you need help.

Ms. Sanders is the (principal / principle) of our school. Our nation is founded on the (principals / principles) of freedom and justice for all people.

4. Is the underlined word a preposition or an adverb?

I looked all <u>around</u>, but no one was there.

preposition     adverb

5. What is the subject of this imperative?

Read the next chapter and take careful notes. ______________

6. Write the word with its suffix.

appreciate + -ion ➡ ______________________________

7. What does this editing mark tell you to do? ¶

______________________________________________________

8. Complete the analogy. Brazil is to South America as _______ is to Europe.

London Spain Mexico Africa

9. Insert a semicolon between the independent clauses.

Lashae tried the door it was locked from the inside.

10. What is the antecedent of the relative pronoun in this sentence?

All of the spectators <u>whose</u> seats are in the top row get the best view.

____________________________

11 – 12. See if you can arrange these words, which are borrowed from the French language, in the chart below. Use a dictionary if you need help.

camouflage entrepreneur mauve du jour

| French Word | Meaning |
|---|---|
| | of the day |
| | business person |
| | disguise |
| | a purplish color |

## Lesson #50

1. **The present participle always ends in *–ing* and is used with a helping verb.**
**Example:** Lori <u>is petting</u> the lambs. The Jacksons <u>are traveling</u> all day.
Underline the present participle and helping verb.

We were painting the fence.

2. **A demonstrative may also be an adjective**. Remember, an adjective modifies a noun. **Example:** <u>Those</u> lemons are fresh.
Underline the demonstrative adjective.

Rita played that song at her recital.

Here are some adverbs that tell *where:* inside, outside, upstairs, downstairs, far, forward, here, somewhere. Many of these words can also be prepositions, but remember, **an adverb modifies a verb; a preposition begins a prepositional phrase.** Look at the underlined words. Write A if the word is an adverb; write P if it is a preposition.

3. _____ The painters are still working <u>somewhere</u>.

4. _____ I'm not sure if they are <u>inside</u> the house.

5 – 8. Read the following writing sample and use editing marks to correct eight errors.

Crayola has been called the most popular brand of crayon. Since 1903, children and and adults have been using crayola in all the colors of the Rainbow - and many more - to create their works of art. today there are 120 colors, including mango tango, raspberry jam, and piggy pink New colors are being developed all the time, and sum older colors been "retired." What happens to a retired Crayola color? It goes straight to the Crayola Hall of fame!

9 – 12. Rewrite the sentences about Crayola correctly and complete the checklist below.

____ Is the paragraph indented?

____ Does every sentence have a subject and a verb?

____ Do the subjects and verbs agree?

____ Do pronouns and antecedents agree?

____ Are all of the proper nouns capitalized? Does each sentence begin with a capital letter?

____ Are commas, apostrophes, and end marks used correctly?

____ Are all the words spelled correctly?

____ Have unnecessary words been removed?

## Lesson #51

1. Write the past, present participle, and past participle of the verb.

| Present | Past | Present Participle | Past Participle |
|---|---|---|---|
| walk | | | |

2. List the four demonstratives.

__________ __________ __________ __________

3. My parents were shocked by the brevity of our school concert; usually, it goes on for ninety minutes or more. From the context clues, you can tell that another word for *brevity* is ________.

A) proficiency B) talent C) deficiency D) shortness

4. Is the underlined word an adjective or an adverb?

The crack is so small, you'll hardly notice it.

adjective adverb

5. **Interjections have a specific purpose and are not used very often in formal writing.** However, interjections are often found in written dialogue. Add the proper punctuation and quotation marks.

Stop Put your hands in the air, shouted the police officer.

6. Use a conjunction to join these sentences. Write the compound sentence.

We raked leaves all afternoon. We played football after dinner.

________________________________________

________________________________________

7. Choose the correct pronoun. (Hint: Would you say "He will" or "Him will?")

(Who / Whom) will be your partner?

8. Underline two antonyms.

prewar postwar postdate reevaluate

9. Dozens of nouveau (noo-vō') shops and cafés opened up along the boulevard. The underlined French word probably means what?

"difficult" "a place to eat" "new or fashionable" "in reality"

10. Draw a line under the subject and choose the verb that agrees with it.

Memorable events, that happened during my lifetime, (are / is) recorded in this journal.

11. **Proof It!** Use two different editing marks to correct errors in the following sentence.

Everyone will be aloud to bring a small suitcase, backpack, tote bag.

12. Rewrite the sentence correctly below.

______________________________________________

______________________________________________

## Lesson #52

1. Write the past, present participle, and past participle of the verb.

| Present | Past | Present Participle | Past Participle |
|---|---|---|---|
| clean | | | |

2. Is the demonstrative in this sentence a pronoun or an adjective?

These are my sisters. pronoun adjective

3. Look in a dictionary or thesaurus and find a better word for *sad*. Write your word on the line.

____________________

4. Write the word with its suffix.

merry + -ly ➡ ____________________

5. Read the sentence; list one adjective and one adverb.

The yard looks stunning; the hedges are neatly trimmed.

Adjective ➡ ____________ Adverb ➡ ____________

6. Choose the verb that agrees.

The Empire State Building (is / are / were) over 1400 feet tall!

7 – 12. You have learned about seven different kinds of pronouns. You can use a graphic organizer to sort out all the types of pronouns and keep track of how you will use them. Complete the chart with information about pronouns. The first one has been done for you. (You can find all the information you need in the *Help Pages*.)

| Pronoun Organizer | | |
|---|---|---|
| Types of pronouns | Examples | How they are used |
| Demonstrative | this, that, these, those | point out something |
| Indefinite | | |
| Interrogative | | |
| Nominative | | |
| Objective | | |
| Possessive | | |
| Relative | | |

## Lesson #53

Study the prefix chart. Then use the word list to complete the three sentences that follow.

| auto- | self | autofocus |
|---|---|---|
| geo- | earth | geochemistry |
| mono- | one | monochrome |

1. I know Phyllis only likes to wear blue, but her ______________________ clothing is so boring!

2. Lawrence wants to study ________________________________ to learn more about minerals, soil, rocks, water, and the atmosphere.

3. The camera has an ________________________________ feature, so just point and click.

4. Underline the adverb that tells *when.*

   We often visit our grandmother in Tennessee.

5. **Sometimes the subject of the sentence comes after the verb. Don't be fooled – subject and verb must agree! Example:** Among the crowd of protesters was a young man named Luke. (The subject and verb are underlined.) Choose the verb that agrees.

   Among my all-time favorite films (are / is) *Gone With the Wind.*

6. Choose the word that has the proper connotation for this sentence. Use a dictionary if you need help.

   Benjamin Franklin was (notorious / famous) for his many inventions and the discovery of electricity.

7. Underline the metaphor. What two things are being compared?

Jarrod is a pitching machine! He never gets tired of throwing the ball.

______________________________ and ______________________________

8. What does a declarative sentence do?

tells something asks something

gives a command shows strong feeling

9. Which is a **cause** and which is an **effect**? Write C or E.

_____ Because Brianna wants to be an athletic trainer, _____ she decided to get a degree in exercise science.

Use the following paragraph to complete the next three items.

Traveling by car through our nation's capital is a hassle! Traffic jams, parking dilemmas, and train delays. The crowds are annoying, and a person could get lost. Touring Washington D.C. on a chartered bus is an **alternative** to travelling by car. A good tour guide can save visitors time, aggravation, and money!

10. Underline a sentence that states a fact.

11. Choose a synonym for the word *alternative*.

vehicle interchange substitute quandary

12. Cross out the fragment and rewrite it as a complete sentence below.

______________________________________________________________

______________________________________________________________

______________________________________________________________

## Lesson #54

1. The prefix *chrono-* means "according to time." Which list is in *chronological* order?

   A) 107, 17, 27, 37 B) first, second, third, fourth C) AA, BA, AB, BB

2. Here is a list of adverbs that tell *when*. Choose one and use it in a sentence of your own.

   Adverbs That Tell *When*

| | | | |
|---|---|---|---|
| after | frequently | seldom | later |
| until | permanently | usually | never |
| again | tomorrow | today | always |
| late | afterwards | while | when |
| since | yesterday | now | soon |
| before | occasionally | still | early |
| earlier | sometimes | often | yet |
| finally | whenever | then | once |

______________________________________________

______________________________________________

3. Choose the verb that agrees.

   Just beyond the wooded area, (live / lives) an elderly couple.

4. **An acronym is defined as "a word formed from the initial letters of other words." Examples:** NATO, UNESCO Look in a dictionary or online to find the meaning of NATO or UNESCO, and write the meaning here.

______________________________________________

______________________________________________

5. Which word completes this analogy?

   __________ is to *journalist* as *building* is to *carpenter*.

   Singing Construction Reporting Factual

6. Underline the complete predicate.

Astrology is a science that studies celestial bodies.

7. Choose the correct homophones.

I (knew / new) we had parked the car in the lot over (their / there).

8. **Insert a comma after an interjection at the beginning of a sentence.**
**Example:** Wow, that test was brutal ! Add a comma to this sentence.

Oh no we're late!

9. In which list are there no capitalization errors?

A) cairo, Egypt; and Israel
B) Cairo, Egypt; and israel
C) Cairo, Egypt; and Israel
D) Cairo, Egypt; And Israel

10. Does the pronoun agree with its antecedent? Yes No

The flock of geese flew behind their leader.

11 – 12. **Proof It!** Rewrite each sentence correctly.

Lisa Anderson began surffing (sp) when ^ just 13 years old (.) Lisa she became a
she was

world champion and a role model for ^ surfers.
female

_______________________________________________

_______________________________________________

_______________________________________________

_______________________________________________

## Lesson #55

1. Since *geo-* refers to "the earth" and *chrono-* means "time," the word *geochronology* is probably the study of _____________.

   A) the smallest living things
   B) all the water on earth
   C) the intensity of light
   D) the age of rock formations

2. Draw a line under the subject and choose the verb that agrees with it.

   Classes throughout the building (was / were) disrupted by the false alarm.

**A circle with a diagonal line is the international symbol for "no." This symbol is used – with other graphics – to tell us that something is not allowed.**

3. What do you think this symbol means?

   ______________________________

   ______________________________

4. **Capitalize the names of religions and races. Examples:** Muslim, Hindi, Asian-American Write this sentence correctly.

   There is a large latino community in the miami area.

   ______________________________

5. Add a comma.

   Oh I thought that was my glass.

6. Write the word with its suffix.

   measure + -ment ➡ ______________________________

7. Complete the sentence with a form of the verb *be* that agrees with the subject.

   The wooden toys _______________ made by hand.

8 – 12. You can use a comparison-contrast matrix to organize information about two items that have similarities and differences. Study the matrix below, and use it to write a short paragraph about two games that just about anyone can play. Bocce and Cornhole are popular at carnivals, field days, picnics, and family reunions.

| ↓ Categories ↓ | Cornhole | Bocce |
|---|---|---|
| Also Called | Corn Toss | Lawn Bowling |
| Equipment | 2 Cornhole boxes, 2 X 4 ft. each<br>8 corn bags in two colors | 1 small white ball (pallino)<br>8 larger balls in two colors |
| Number of players | 2 teams, with one or two players per team | 2 teams, with one, two, or four players per team |
| Who can play | children and adults | children and adults |
| Where played | outdoors or in a large room | a grassy yard or bocce court |
| How to score | pitch the bags onto the box, near or into the hole | pitch or roll the ball as close as possible to the pallino |
| Score needed to win | 21 points | 16 points |

## Lesson #56

1. **What is the difference between an abbreviation and an acronym? Some abbreviations are taken from the first letter of each word and are pronounced letter by letter:** PTA, TV, and NBA. **Acronyms are like that, but they are pronounced as words:** NASA, NATO, and BASIC.

   Circle the acronyms. OPEC NFL SCUBA IRS

2. Complete the analogy. *Conceal* is to ___________ as *nervous* is to *calm*.

   hide locate reveal confide

3. **Insert a comma after introductory words. Example:** *On the other hand*, the interest rates may go up. Place a comma where it is needed.

   By the way are you coming to my party?

4. Look at the underlined words. If there is an error, choose the correction. If there is no error, choose "correct as is."

   Many south africans immigrated from India and Europe.

   A) south Africans B) South Africans C) South africans D) correct as is

5. Underline the collective noun; choose the correct verb.

   A brood of chicks (have / has) been nesting near that pond.

6. Write the plural form of each.

   worry ➡ _______________ strawberry ➡ ___________________

7. The mother bird gently nudged the fledglings out of the nest. What is the meaning of the underlined word?

   baby birds tree branches a bird's nest a type of hawk

8 – 12. Make a comparison-contrast chart of your own. Compare any two things that have some similarities and some differences. Choose two things that you know a lot about: favorite TV shows, sports, types of music, pets, classes, or just about anything. Use the outline below.

| ↓ Categories ↓ | | |
|---|---|---|
| | | |
| | | |
| | | |
| | | |

# Lesson #57

1. Insert a comma after the introductory word.

   Suddenly there were over a hundred people lined up along the path.

2. Look at the underlined words. If there is an error, choose the correction. If there is no error, choose "correct as is."

   Nelson Mandela wrote *the struggle is my life*.

   A) *The Struggle Is My Life* C) the Struggle is My Life

   B) *the Struggle is my Life* D) correct as is

3. Choose the verb that agrees.

   It's raining and nobody (have / has) an umbrella.

4. Study the definitions and choose the correct homophone to complete each sentence.

   compliment ➡ (*noun*): praise, encouraging comment

   complement ➡ (*noun*): something that completes another thing

   "The Spring Recital was very balanced this year," commented Pia. "Yes," Marla agreed. "The piano solos were a nice (compliment / complement) to the choir performances. And did you notice that the music instructor gave Kaliani a (compliment / complement) on her rendition of Fleur-de-lis?"

5. **When a word ends in a consonant plus *y*, change the *y* to *i* before adding most suffixes. But if the suffix is *–ing*, do not change the *–y* to *–i*.**
   **Examples:** carrying, trying Write the word with its suffix.

   hurry + -ing ➡ ______________________

6. Choose the possessive pronoun that correctly completes the sentence.

   The winning entry is (ours / our).

7. Read these two statements. Put a C next to the **cause** and an E next to the **effect**.

____ In 1962 Fannie Lou Hammer demanded the right to register as a voter.

____ As a result of that action, Fannie Lou and her family were forced out of their home.

8. **A subordinate (dependent) clause does not express a complete thought and cannot stand on its own. Example:** Before I go home, I need to stop at the dry cleaners. Underline the subordinate clause in this sentence.

While we were away, the pipes in the kitchen froze.

9. What is a demonstrative?

A) a pronoun that refers to a particular thing or place

B) an adjective that modifies a noun

C) may be either a pronoun or an adjective

10. What is being compared in the two similes in this sentence?

The kids swarmed like bees around the piñata, which clung tight as a well-built beehive to the low rafters in the shelter.

______________________ ______________________

11. Draw a line under the complete subject.

The children, dripping wet and cold from being caught in the rainstorm, huddled together near a crackling fire.

12. **Words containing *-graph-* or *-gram-* are from the Greek and have to do with writing, drawing, or recording.** See if you can match the words in this list with their meanings in the chart below.

cartography homograph seismograph biography

| | |
|---|---|
| A) | word that is written like another word |
| B) | records movement of the earth |
| C) | drawing maps |
| D) | the story of someone's life |

## Lesson #58

1. **Use a comma after an adverb clause that comes at the beginning of a sentence. Example:** *After the rainfall,* we played in the mud. (*After the rainfall* modifies *played.*) Insert a comma after the adverb clause.

   Before we graduate we will complete a service project.

2. Look at the underlined words. If there is an error, choose the correction. If there is no error, choose "correct as is."

   I like chinese food, but Mexican food is my favorite.

   A) I like Chinese Food
   C) I like chinese Food
   B) I like Chinese food
   D) correct as is

3. Choose the correct verb.

   Lewis and Clark (is / are / was) honored as brave and intelligent explorers.

4. Write the word with its suffix. bury + -ing ➡ ____________________

5. Put a ✓ next to the sentence that states a fact.

   ____ Many public buildings prohibit smoking.

   ____ The smoking ban makes life healthier and more pleasant for a lot of people.

6. My ______________ is the story of my life.

   biography autobiography chronology bibliography

7. Underline the object pronoun that correctly completes the sentence.

   Ask Dad if he can take Billy and (I / me) to soccer practice.

8. He is called the president, but his practices make him the *de facto* dictator. The Latin term in italics probably means what?

   "in fact" "in case" "otherwise" "all together"

9. **A subordinate (dependent) clause can be a noun clause, an adjective clause, or an adverb clause, but it must be used with a main clause. Example:** Because they are nocturnal, the snakes hunt after dark. (The subordinate clause is underlined. Notice that the subordinate clause has its own subject and verb, but it would not make sense without the main clause.)
Underline the subordinate clause in this sentence.

Although the house was dark, I was not afraid.

**Subordinating conjunctions are used to join a subordinate clause to a main clause.**
**Example:** Please do not use the cell phone *unless* there is an emergency.
Here some examples of subordinating conjunctions:

| | | | | |
|---|---|---|---|---|
| after | before | if | though | whenever |
| although | even if | since | unless | where |
| as | even though | than | until | wherever |
| because | how | that | when | while |

10. Write a sentence of your own using one of the subordinating conjunctions.

_______________________________________________

_______________________________________________

11. Look at the underlined adverb. Does it tell *how*, *when*, *where*, or *to what extent*?

Holding a magnet near your tape will permanently erase it.

_______________________

12. Write the past, present participle, and past participle of the verb.

| Present | Past | Present Participle | Past Participle |
|---|---|---|---|
| plant | | | |

## Lesson #59

1. Insert a comma after the adverb clause.

   With all her might Gina resisted the tug of the undertow.

2. Choose the verb that agrees.

   The most important rule among good friends (are / is) "Be honorable."

3. Write the word with its suffix.

   happy + -ness ➡ ______________________________

4. Underline the subordinate clause in this sentence.

   We usually buy a souvenir whenever we visit another state.

5. Choose the correct homophones.

   We tried to give away (hour / our) puppies

   by putting an (ad / add) in the newspaper.

6. Three of these words are synonyms; cross out the word that does not belong in this list.

   drawings graphics portfolios illustrations

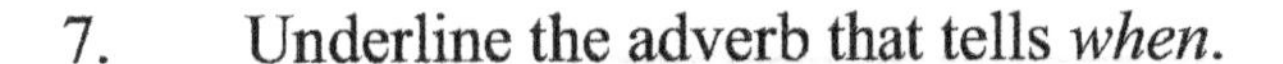

7. Underline the adverb that tells *when*.

   Did you finish the story yet?

8. What is the meaning of this symbol? © (Look in the *Help Pages* if you are not sure.)

   ______________________________________________

9. Underline the subject pronoun.

(We / Us) and the rest of the gang will meet you at the dock.

10. My mother is on a bus to Chicago, but she may be able to speak to you en route if you call her cell phone. What is the meaning of the underlined French phrase?

on the way  if you please  of the day  in writing

11. What is missing from this fragment?  subject  verb

The scary-looking house at the end of my street.

Rewrite the fragment as a complete sentence below.

_______________________________________________

_______________________________________________

12. Write the past, present participle, and past participle of the verb.

| Present | Past | Present Participle | Past Participle |
| --- | --- | --- | --- |
| stop | | | |

## Lesson #60

1. **Use a comma after a prepositional phrase, at the beginning of a sentence, if the phrase has five or more words. Examples:** *On the south side of the house,* there is an iron gate. (The prepositional phrase has seven words; a comma is needed.) *Along the path* there are some orange lilies. (The prepositional phrase is short, so no comma is needed.) Insert a comma wherever necessary.

   Under your chair there is a card with a number written on it.

   Along with the numbered card there is a small package.

2. Choose the verb that agrees.

   The leader elected by the women (were / was) Mrs. Price.

3. Underline the words that best complete the sentence.

   Is there enough room for (us and the neighbors / the neighbors and us) on the patio?

4. Write the word with its suffix.

   fancy + -ful ➡ ______________________________

5. Have you seen this symbol? What does it mean?

   ______________________________

   ______________________________

6. Underline the subordinate clause in this sentence.

   Don't make any noise while the baby is sleeping.

7. A <u>single</u> speaker performs which of these?

   conversation monologue debate dialogue

8. Choose the correct homophones.

Because of an accident, the (right / write) lane of the (road /rode) was entirely blocked.

9. Underline the verb and circle the adverb that tells *when.*

Sometimes Mr. Thompson gives a pop quiz.

10. Which pair of words completes this analogy? doe : fawn :: _____ : _____

bird : flock     cow : bull     goose : gosling     mouse : mice

11. Write the past, present participle, and past participle of the verb.

| Present | Past | Present Participle | Past Participle |
|---|---|---|---|
| play | | | |

12. See if you can arrange these words, which are borrowed from the Dutch language, in the chart below. Use a dictionary if you need help.

knapsack     yacht     ahoy     caboose

| Dutch Word | Meaning |
|---|---|
| A) | a sailing vessel |
| B) | car at the end of a train |
| C) | a leather bag |
| D) | a greeting used by sailors |

## Lesson #61

**Indefinite pronouns have no specific antecedent. They may be singular or plural, but an indefinite pronoun must agree with the verb in a sentence.**
**Example:** Everyone *is* present. Somebody always *brings* lunch.

**These indefinite pronouns are singular and must be paired with singular verbs.**

| | | | | |
|---|---|---|---|---|
| another | each | everything | nobody | other |
| anybody | either | little | no one | somebody |
| anyone | everybody | much | nothing | someone |
| anything | everyone | neither | one | something |

1. Choose the verb that agrees with each singular indefinite pronoun.

   There are two containers; one (carry / carries) the paper and the other (hold / holds) the paint.

2. Choose another indefinite pronoun from the chart and use it in a sentence of your own.

   ______________________________________________

   ______________________________________________

3. Insert a comma wherever it is needed. (Hint: Look at the previous lesson to review the rule.)

   Down the street there are more shops. Throughout the rest of the town the shops will be closed.

4. **Irregular verbs also have four principal parts. But irregular verbs do not use *-ed* to form the past tense. Example:** swim - swam - swum. Look in the *Help Pages* for more examples of irregular verbs. Write the present, past, and past participle of three irregular verbs here:

| Present | Past | Past Participle |
|---|---|---|
| | | |
| | | |
| | | |

5. What is the meaning of the French word in the following sentence?

Roger blushed with embarrassment at his obvious faux pas (fō pä').

a dear friend  a type of food  a mistake  a business letter

Study the definitions and choose the correct homophone to complete each sentence.

assent ➡ (*verb*) to agree or go along with

ascent ➡ (*noun*) an upward movement

6. My parents will never (assent / ascent) to a three-night sleepover.

7. Even experienced climbers will find the (assent / ascent) challenging.

8. **If a word ends in a vowel and -*y*, do not change the -*y* before adding a suffix.**
**Example:** destroy + -ed ➡ destroyed  Write the word with its suffix.

employ + -er ➡ ______________________

9. Fill in a pronoun that agrees with the collective noun.

The government is complicated; __________ has many parts.

10. Underline the verb in this sentence. What kind is it – action, linking, or helping?

No one was at home. ______________________

11. A simile compares two things, using the words *like* or *as*. Complete the following sentence with a simile.

Perry raced through the yard ______________________

______________________________________________.

12. A metaphor compares but does not use the words *like* or *as*. Complete the following sentence with a metaphor.

My first day at summer camp was ______________________

______________________________________________.

# Lesson #62

**Indefinite pronouns may be singular or plural but they must agree with the verb in a sentence.** Many of the guests *are* in the living room; others *are* in the back yard.

**These indefinite pronouns are plural and must be paired with plural verbs.**

both few many others several

1. Choose the verbs that agree with the plural indefinite pronouns.

   A few of the passengers (has / have) helmets. However, several (is / are) not even wearing safety belts.

2. Insert a comma after the prepositional phrase.

   Except for a few of yesterday's leftovers the refrigerator is empty.

3. **Insert a comma after introductory words in an imperative or interjection.**
   **Examples:** Oh no, we are out of snacks. Darla, would you go to the store?
   Add a comma to this sentence.

   Ms. Wyatt_ would you like some iced tea?

**Use commas before and after interrupting words or phrases within a sentence.**
**Examples:** Please, Jackson, show Mrs. Ellery your work. Dinner, of course, will be served in the dining room. (Notice that you can remove the interrupting word or phrase and still have a complete sentence.) Insert commas before and after the interrupting phrase in the following sentences.

4. You know since you saw the news that there is a tornado watch in effect this evening.

5. Please pay attention boys and girls while I give the directions.

6. Underline the word with the appropriate connotation.

   I enjoy talking to my uncle, because he is always very (curious / nosey) about the things I like to do.

Study the examples in the chart, and fill in the empty spaces.

| Principal Parts of Irregular Verbs | | | |
|---|---|---|---|
| Present | Past | Present Participle | Past Participle |
| shine | shone | shining | has shone |
| do | did | doing | have done |
| 7. draw | | | |
| 8. begin | | | |
| 9. spin | | | |

10. The prefix *dia-* means "across" or "apart."

The distance across a circle is its ________________.

diamond diameter diatribe

11. **Use a comma before and/or after a quote within a sentence. Example:** "The music was interesting," commented Jamie, "but the dialogue was confusing." (Notice how the commas set off each part so that the meaning is clear.) Insert commas.

"Everyone is present" announced Mrs. Rob "so we can begin."

12. **Proof It!** Rewrite the following sentence correctly.

On a cool October evening I visited my neice near the thames.

_______________________________________________

_______________________________________________

## Lesson #63

1. Place commas before and after the interrupting phrase.

   The rainfall although it was heavy only lasted a short time.

2. Which word completes the analogy? *Bird* is to *aviary* as *fish* is to ________.

   ocean aquarium whale zoo

**These indefinite pronouns can be either singular or plural; it depends on how they are used in a sentence. Examples:** Most of the house is clean. (*Most* refers to house--one thing--so *most* is singular.) Some of the birds are cardinals. (*Some* refers to birds, which is plural.)

all any more most none some

3. Decide whether the indefinite pronouns are singular or plural, and choose the verbs that agree.

   Most of the cake (was / were) eaten, but none of the white plates (was / were) used.

4. Write the plural form of each of the nouns. Use a dictionary to check your work.

   quartz ➡ ________________ tractor ➡ ________________

   hoof ➡ ________________

5. Write the word with its suffix.

   destroy + -er ➡ ________________

6. Insert commas to complete this quote.

   "Everywhere you look" marveled Elaine "there are dozens of roses."

7. Underline the adverb that tells *when.*

   Carla cleans the refrigerator frequently.

Study the partial flight schedule and airline codes shown below, and use them to answer the last five questions.

| FLIGHT | ARRIVAL | DEPARTURE | AIRCRAFT | FLIGHT DAYS | ROUTE |
|---|---|---|---|---|---|
| 906 | 5:00 AM | 7:00 AM | 737-400 | MTWTFSS | PSP-SFO-SEA |
| 695 | 11:19 AM | 11:40 AM | 737-400 | SS | BOI-SLC |
| 3922 | 12:42 PM | 1:00 PM | 737-400 | MTWTFSS | IAH-DFW-PHX |
| 798 | 3:14 PM | 5:01 PM | 737-400 | TFSS | PHX-PSP-LAS |
| 6140 | 8:59 PM | 10:06 PM | 737-400 | M W FSS | DEN-PSP |

| AIRPORT CODES | | | | | |
|---|---|---|---|---|---|
| ANC | Anchorage, AK | IAH | Houston, TX | SEA | Seattle, WA |
| BOI | Boise, ID | LAS | Las Vegas, NV | SLC | Salt Lake City, UT |
| DEN | Denver, CO | PHX | Phoenix, AZ | SFO | San Francisco, CA |
| DFW | Dallas/Fort Worth, TX | PSP | Palm Springs, CA | SMF | Sacramento, CA |

8. Which airport uses the initials IAH?

_______________________________________________

9. On which days of the week is there a flight from Boise, Idaho to Salt Lake City, Utah?

_______________________________________________

10. What is the departure time for flight 6140 on Mondays?

_______________________________________________

11. How many cities are listed in the route for flight 798?

_______________________________________________

12. Is there a flight scheduled from Phoenix to Palm Springs on Wednesdays?

_______________________________________________

## Lesson #64

1. Underline the verb that agrees with the indefinite pronoun.

   Choose one of these dates; either (are / is) available right now.

2. **Insert a comma before and/or after contrasting phrases within a sentence. Example:** Let's use whole wheat flour, rather than white flour, in the bread. Insert two commas.

   I'll take relish and mustard not ketchup on my hot dog.

3. **The present participle always ends in *–ing* and is used with a helping verb. Example:** Lori *is petting* the lambs. The Jacksons *are traveling* all day. Underline the present participle and helping verb.

   We were painting the fence.

4 – 5. Write the past, present participle, and past participle of the following irregular verbs (hint: use the *Help Pages*).

| Present | Past | Present Participle | Past Participle |
|---|---|---|---|
| bear | | | |
| deal | | | |

6. **It is not necessary to use a comma at the end of a quote if there is another punctuation mark. Example:** "Look at all the balloons!" cried Georgie. "Can we get one?" Insert quotation marks and end punctuation.

   When will the pizza be ready asked Reyna I'm hungry

7. The Greek root *bronte* means "thunder;" *sauros* means "lizard." (You can imagine the thunderous sound of a brontosaurus walking across the earth!) What do you think *brontophobia* is?

   A) a type of dinosaur
   B) a fear of lizards
   C) fear of thunder
   D) none of these

8 – 12. Read the prompt and write a draft of at least five sentences.

If you could change your school calendar - without reducing the number of days of school - how would you do it? For example, would you go to school year-round but take more long breaks throughout the year? Or, would you be willing to go to school six days a week and have a longer vacation? Explain your rationale.

# Lesson #65

1. Write the past and past participle of the verb *buy*.

   ____________________, had ____________________

**There are three perfect verb tenses in English; they all use past tense verbs plus the helping verbs *had, has,* or *have*.** Study the chart below and then complete the next three items.

| Perfect Tenses of Regular Verbs | | | |
|---|---|---|---|
| | Present Perfect | Past Perfect | Future Perfect |
| Use of the Verb | Shows action that is ongoing or indefinite. | Shows which thing happened first. (Both happened in the past.) | Shows what will happen before something else in the future. |
| Helping Verbs | *has* or *have* | *had* | *will have* |
| Example (singular subject) | Nick *has finished* two of his assignments. | She *had asked* for help before she started working. | I *will have completed* everything by bedtime. |
| Example (plural subject) | We *have played* soccer for many years. | The children *had napped* earlier that afternoon. | We *will have learned* the routines by then. |

2. Complete the sentence by adding the present perfect form of the verb *climb*.

   Brave explorers ______________ ______________ Mount Everest for many years.

3. Complete the sentence by adding the past perfect form of the verb *climb*.

   My uncle ______________ ______________ a smaller mountain before he joined the Everest team.

4. Complete the sentence by adding the future perfect form of the verb *climb*.

   By the end of the decade, Uncle Norris ______________ ______________ ______________ three more mountains.

5. Decide whether the indefinite pronoun is singular or plural, and choose the verb that agrees.

   None of the landscaping (were / was) in need of water.

6. **Insert commas before and after contrasting phrases**. Place two commas in this sentence.

The fireworks are at Baxley Park not Euclid Square tonight.

7. A ______________________ occurs between two parties.

monologue dialogue speech soliloquy

Read the excerpt from Donna's poem. Then complete the next three items.

Listening to a soft chorus of cicadas,
Slowly cascading, then slipping into a crescendo
Like the shrill sirens of cop cars
On a hot summer night in Cleveland

8. What two things are being compared in the simile?

A) listening and cascading
B) a crescendo and cop cars
C) a soft chorus and a hot summer night
D) the sound of cicadas and the sound of sirens

9. Based on what the poem says, Donna was probably listening to

A) night sounds
B) a fountain
C) her favorite song
D) the crowd at a baseball game

10. Which phrase tells how the sound was flowing and getting softer and then began to get louder?

A) a soft chorus of cicadas
B) cascading then slipping into a crescendo
C) the shrill sirens of cop cars
D) All of the above

**Proof It!** Use two different editing marks to correct errors in each of these sentences.

11. The people of Mexico when celebrate independence Day on September 16.

12. Puerto Rico's Independence Day is celebreated on July 4, Since it is a U.S. territory.

## Lesson #66

**Irregular verbs also use the helping verbs *had, has,* or *have* to form the three perfect tenses**. Study the chart below and then complete the next three items.

| Perfect Tenses of Irregular Verbs | | | |
|---|---|---|---|
| | Present Perfect | Past Perfect | Future Perfect |
| Use of the Verb | Shows action that is ongoing or indefinite. | Shows which thing happened first. (Both happened in the past.) | Shows what will happen before something else in the future. |
| Helping Verbs | *has* or *have* | *had* | *will have* |
| Example (singular subject) | That dog *has bitten* kids on our block. | You *had eaten* a snack just before dinner. | Sam *will have strung* all the beads together by tonight. |
| Example (plural subject) | They *have forgiven* our numerous errors. | Wilma and Ed *had heard* that song before. | By the end of camp, We *will have met* everyone. |

1. Complete the sentence by adding the present perfect form of the verb *win*.

   Our team members ______________ ______________ many awards.

2. Complete the sentence by adding the past perfect form of the verb *win*.

   Noah ______________ ______________ a medal for his science project last year.

3. Complete the sentence by adding the future perfect form of the verb *win*.

   I hope that all of us ____________ ______________ ______________ honors by the time we leave this school.

4. Underline the indefinite pronoun, and choose the verb that agrees.

   Everything (was / were) clearer after the storm.

5. **Use a comma to separate consecutive words or numbers, when writing a date.**
   **Examples:** Monday, July 3     February 2, 2007     Insert commas.

   Jacob Henry was born on Monday July 17 2006.

6. Add the proper punctuation to this interjection.

Look out That shelf is about to fall.

7. Complete the following analogy. *Valid* is to *validation* as ____ is to *corruption.*

unacceptable dishonesty corrupt improper

8. Here is a list of adverbs that tell *to what extent.* Choose one from the list and use it in a sentence of your own.

Adverbs That Tell *To What Extent*

| thoroughly | barely | completely | very | scarcely | also |
|---|---|---|---|---|---|
| vaguely | more | extremely | quite | rather | too |

______________________________________________

9. Fill in a conjunction to complete the sentence.

Please sign up for the marathon _______ the relay race.

10. Smokey Bear is a staunch protector of wild life. What is the meaning of the underlined word?

meager firm weak temporary

11 – 12. **Proof It!** People speak in run-on sentences, but run-ons are grammatically incorrect and difficult to understand in writing. Rewrite this run-on so that it makes sense. You can break it up into smaller sentences, and you can use conjunctions to make the sentences clearer.

Malaria is a deadly disease it is carried by mosquitoes people in places that have a lot of rain and stagnant water get malaria it causes weakness, chills, and fever people sometimes die from it if they do not have medication.

______________________________________________

______________________________________________

______________________________________________

## Lesson #67

1. Write the plural of *torpedo*. ______________________

2. Decide whether the indefinite pronoun is singular or plural, and choose the other pronoun that agrees.

   Most of the newspaper is mangled, so you may not be able to read (it / them).

3. Words with the Latin roots *-jur-*, *-jud-*, or *-jus-* have to do with law or what is right. See if you can match the words in this list with their meanings in the chart below.

   jury    justice    abjure    just

| | |
|---|---|
| A) | lawful |
| B) | fairness, honesty |
| C) | a group of people who decide what is right |
| D) | to give up one's rights |

4. Underline the adverb that tells *when.*

   Afterwards, we played football in the yard.

5. Add commas where necessary.

   On Tuesday September 5 we will return to class, and we'll have another holiday on Monday October 17.

6. Think about the connotation of each of the two words listed below. Then sort this list of synonyms by writing them underneath the word that matches its connotation. One of each has been done for you.

   antagonistic    confident    hostile    self-assured    pushy    forward

| Assertive | Aggressive |
|---|---|
| firm | forceful |

7. What is the meaning of this symbol? @ (Look in the *Help Pages* if you are not sure.)

_______________________________________________

8. Underline each interjection.

Hey, what's up? Oh boy, have I got news for you!

9. Choose the conjunction that best completes this sentence.

Neither my mother (and/or/nor) my father was born in the United States.

10. Find the word *suffragist* in a thesaurus or dictionary. Underline its meaning.

someone who is very ill

someone who causes great pain to others

someone who supports the right to vote

**Proof It!** Use two editing marks to correct errors in each of the following sentences.

11. If you enjoy to looking at bugs, you may want to become entomologist.

12. entomologists are scientists that investigate insects — how they interract with the environment and affect the lives of people.

## Lesson #68

1. Choose the verb that agrees with the indefinite pronoun.

   All of the stage (is / are) brightly painted.

2. Jon's ____________________ is a story he has written about himself.

   biography autobiography chronology bibliography

3. Underline the adverb that tells *to what extent*.

   Wait until the paint dries thoroughly before you close the window.

4. What is the meaning of this symbol? **&** (Look in the *Help Pages* if you are not sure.)

   ______________________________________________

5. Add a comma after each interjection.

   Oh I see you made yourself at home. Well you'd better make a list of things to do.

6 – 7 Match these words, borrowed from the Arabic language, with their meanings. Use a dictionary if you need help.

| | |
|---|---|
| safari | season |
| algebra | the reuniting of parts or pieces |
| zenith | highest point |
| monsoon | a journey |

8 – 12. The English historian James Anthony Froude wrote "Instruction does not prevent wasted time or mistakes; and mistakes themselves are often the best teachers of all." Write about a mistake that taught you something. What happened? What did you learn?

## Lesson #69

1. Underline the verb that agrees with the indefinite pronoun.

   Both (is / are) in the garage.

2. **Homographs are words that are spelled the same but have different meanings, pronunciations, and uses.** Is the underlined homograph used as a verb or a noun?

   Someone will have to keep a <u>record</u> of the students who have brought their permission slips.

   verb noun

3. Is the underlined homograph used as a verb or a noun?

   The team manager asked Rashid to <u>record</u> the statistics during every game.

   verb noun

4. **When writing an address, insert a comma between each separate part. Example:** I live at 6963 Oak Street, Lowellville, Ohio. Insert commas.

   Bertie sent the package to 1420 East Avenue Austin Texas.

5. Three of these words are synonyms; cross out the word that does not belong in this list.

   clever intelligent bizarre bright

6. **A complex sentence contains a subordinate clause and a main clause.** Consider this sentence: You will never guess how I learned to swim! (*You will never guess* is the main clause; *how I learned to swim* is the subordinate clause.) Underline the main clause.

   Do not go into the water unless you have a buddy.

7. Have you seen this symbol? What does it stand for?

______________________________

______________________________

8. What is the meaning of the underlined words? (Use a dictionary if you need help.)

Paulette likes to serve hors d'oeuvres like shrimp, vegetables, or cheese and crackers.

______________________________

9. Remember, *good* is an adjective, so it modifies a noun. The word *well* is an adverb; it modifies a verb. Write *good* or *well* to complete the sentence.

My dinner was very ____________.

10. Find these words in a thesaurus or dictionary. Underline the word that best completes the sentence.

asphalt jalopy irony

The man drove a broken down old ____________ into the service station.

11 – 12. **Proof It!** Draw a line through the fragment, and rewrite it as a complete thought.

If you see a stray dog, it is best not to approach it. Call animal protective services or the local police department. The dog may be injured, hungry, or frightened. Even a dog that has been abused. You may be able to help, but do it safely.

______________________________

______________________________

______________________________

______________________________

______________________________

## Lesson #70

1. Match these subjects with their verbs.

| | |
|---|---|
| Neither | were |
| Several | was |

2. Is the underlined homograph used as a verb or a noun?

My uncle buys and sells produce at the West Side Market.

verb noun

3. **Use a comma after the greeting and the closing in a friendly letter.**
**Examples:** Dear Regis, To Whom This May Concern, Sincerely yours,
Insert five commas where they are needed in the letter.

Dear Mrs. Webster

We have received your order and we shipped your package today. Our records show the following billing address. Please call us right away if the address is incorrect: 9384 Renway Avenue South Chester Illinois.

Sincerely

Pop-Books Publishers

4. **A complex sentence is made up of two clauses (one main and one subordinate) joined by a subordinating conjunction.** Underline the complex sentence.

We like to play the Dreidel Game in December. Usually we make our own dreidels, so that we can play at recess. We play until the paper dreidel falls apart.

5. Have you seen this symbol? What does it stand for?

______________________________

6. Look at these words from the Farsi language. See if you can match each word with its meaning.

| | |
|---|---|
| khaki | a type of nut |
| pistachio | a type of fabric |
| bazaar | a marketplace |

7. **When using the pronouns *I, me, we,* or *us,* it is proper to list them last.**
**Examples:** them and us, Tasha and I, Luke and me
Choose the correct subject of this sentence.

(Me and William / William and I) play football together.

8. What do you think a chronologist studies?

vegetation    water power    living things    time periods

9. Complete the sentence with *good* or *well.*

I wish you ____________________.

10. Add the proper punctuation to this interjection within a quote.

Oops cried the giant.

11. The actor's haughty behavior made everyone feel uncomfortable. What is the meaning of the underlined word?

stuck-up    gracious    pleasant    hilarious

**Proof It!** Rewrite the following sentence correctly.

12. Matthew doesn't feel ~~good~~ well today, so I have (axed) sp his teacher to let you ~~give~~ pick up his homework.

_______________________________________________

_______________________________________________

_______________________________________________

## Lesson #71

1. Complete the sentence with a form of the verb *be* that agrees with the subject.

   Nothing ____________ impossible today!

2. Is the underlined homograph used as a verb or a noun?

   Flora will be our leader, and Eunice will be the alternate.

   verb noun

3. **Use a colon after the greeting in a formal or business letter; use a comma after the closing. Examples:** Dear Mr. Phillips: Sincerely,
   Insert punctuation to make this writing correct.

   Dear Mrs. Fiore

   This letter is to inform you that we have received your application and payment. We look forward to meeting you.

   Sincerely

   Daisy White

4. Monotheism is belief in

   A) one God. B) many gods. C) humanity. D) nothing.

5. A complex sentence is made up of t______________ c______________

   joined by a s__________________ c__________________________.

   (Hint: see previous lesson.)

6. Complete the sentence by adding the present perfect form of the verb *bite*.

   That dog ________________ ______________ other dogs on our street.

7. Underline the object pronoun that correctly completes the sentence.

   Mom prepared lunch for Dallas and (I / me).

## Chain of Events

Sometimes an effect can also be a cause. One thing leads to another and this creates a chain of events. For example, when a student works hard in school, she learns as much as possible. This academic achievement leads to better grades. A student with a high grade point average is more likely to go to college. A college graduate is able to get a higher paying and more satisfying job.

8 – 12. Use the graphic organizer below to summarize the chain of events that you read about in the paragraph above. You do not have to write complete sentences; use phrases from the paragraph to complete each section.

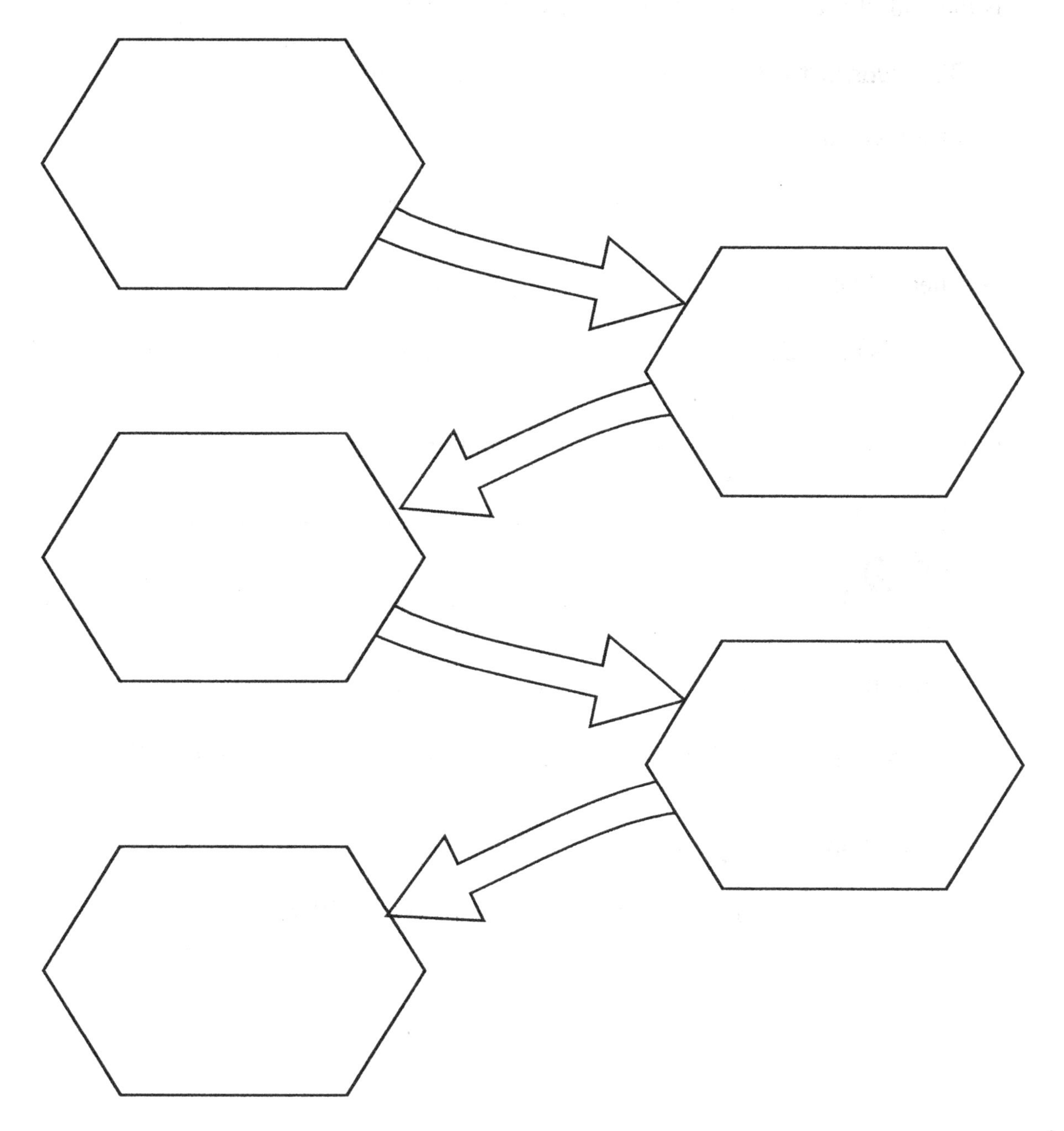

# Lesson #72

1. Are any of these plurals misspelled? Use a dictionary to check. Then write any misspelled words correctly. jellies autos thiefs monkies

_______________________________________________

2. Choose the verbs that agree.

All of the players (is / are) ready, but none of them (have / has) had their lunch break.

3. Is the underlined homograph used as a verb or a noun?

Toni wants to direct and <u>produce</u> a documentary about immigrants in America.

verb noun

4. Geothermal heat comes from what?

A) clouds B) the sun C) water D) the earth

5. Have you seen this symbol? What does it stand for?

_______________________________________________

_______________________________________________

6. Underline the words that best complete the sentence.

The dog chased (me and Troy / Troy and me) all the way home.

7. Choose the adjective or adverb to complete this sentence.

Fred was driving very (wild / wildly).

You have learned about simple, compound, and complex sentences. Here is a summary.

| Structure | Parts | Joined by | Example |
|---|---|---|---|
| Simple | subject & predicate | | Maria Telkes was a brilliant scientist. |
| Compound | two independent clauses | conjunction (and, but, or) | Dr. Telkes became a biophysicist, and she devoted her career to the use of solar energy. |
| Complex | subordinate and main clause | subordinating conjunction | Although she was born in Hungary, Maria immigrated to the United States. |

Read each sentence, and refer to the chart. Then label each sentence as simple, compound, or complex.

8. Before the child labor laws went into effect, children worked as vendors, selling things on city streets.

simple compound complex

9. They sold newspapers, fruits and vegetables, muffins, and flowers.

simple compound complex

10. Many children worked on farms, but they were also able to attend school.

simple compound complex

11 – 12. **Proof It!** Fix this run-on sentence. Rewrite it by adding conjunctions or breaking it up into smaller sentences. Make sure each sentence expresses a complete thought.

Felicity wants to be a journalist she likes to write but she does not enjoy doing research she is more of a creative writer and newspaper reporters have to be willing to investigate maybe she should consider being a novelist instead.

______________________________

______________________________

______________________________

______________________________

## Lesson #73

1. Make these nouns plural.

   chimney beach country laugh

2. Look at the symbols to the right. Put an X over the symbol that means "wheelchair accessible."

3. Isaac's attempt to destroy the model village was <u>deliberate</u>. What is the meaning of the underlined word?

   accidental on purpose fortunate

4. Evaluate these statements. Are they facts, opinions, or a little of both? Explain.

   Consuming sugar-free gum or candy instead of regular sweets is less likely to promote tooth decay. But candy made with artificial sweetener just doesn't taste good.

   ______________________________________________

   ______________________________________________

   ______________________________________________

5. Insert commas before and after contrasting phrases in the following sentence.

   I cleaned the dining room not the kitchen this morning.

6. **Abbreviations are shortened forms of words. Most abbreviations begin with a capital letter and end with a period.** Match each abbreviation with its meaning.

| | |
|---|---|
| Apt. | Post Office |
| Inc. | Apartment |
| P.O. | Incorporated |

7. **You can find a list of abbreviations in a dictionary**. Write the meaning of each abbreviation.

Apr. ➡ ______________________ OH ➡ ________________

Blvd. ➡ ____________________________________

8. Evaluate this sentence. Rewrite it so that the pronoun agrees with the antecedent.

The group lost their folder.

_______________________________________________________

9. Choose the pair that completes the analogy. driver : school bus :: ___ : ___

chicken : hen ink : pen pilot : airplane president : cabinet

Read each sentence, and label it as simple, compound, or complex.

10. There was an overflow where the downspout meets the drain.

simple compound complex

11. Dad and Roger dug a trench, but they didn't have time to finish the job.

simple compound complex

12. Although there was a heavy rain, we did not have any water in the basement.

simple compound complex

## Lesson #74

1. Use context clues to match the underlined phrase with its meaning. Because Dr. Connors had an aversion to flying, he usually rented a car for long trips.

   a keenness for     a dislike of     a talent for     a knowledge of

2. Choose the word with the appropriate connotation for this sentence. (Use a dictionary if you need help.)

   Dermott creates artwork that is colorful and imaginative; his work is very (distinctive / peculiar).

3. **Remember, an adverb modifies a verb.** Is the underlined word used as an adverb or preposition in each sentence?

   Let's eat lunch outside.     adverb     preposition

   The flowers outside the fence are daffodils.     adverb     preposition

4. **A linking verb links the subject of a sentence with a predicate nominative or predicate adjective, which renames or describes the subject.** Underline the linking verb in this sentence.

   Norman seems sleepy today.

5. Circle the predicate adjective in the sentence above.

6. Add a helping verb to form the present perfect tense.

   Bradley ________ been a member of the Youth Symphony for nine years.

7. **A pronoun must agree with its antecedent.** Fill in the pronoun that agrees with the underlined antecedent.

   Carlos and Troy were elated when ______________ discovered the hidden treasure.

8. Choose the verb that agrees with the subject.

   Saravati had (goes / went / gone) back to India to teach at the University.

9. **Remember, a cause tells *why*; an effect tells *what*.** Is the underlined part a cause or an effect?

Gabrielle is lactose intolerant, so she always reads food labels carefully.

cause effect

10 – 12. Use the graphic organizer to outline the steps of something that happens in a cycle. It could be the Water Cycle, steps in the Writing Process, phases of the moon, the cycle of your day, or your own idea.

Title: ______________________________

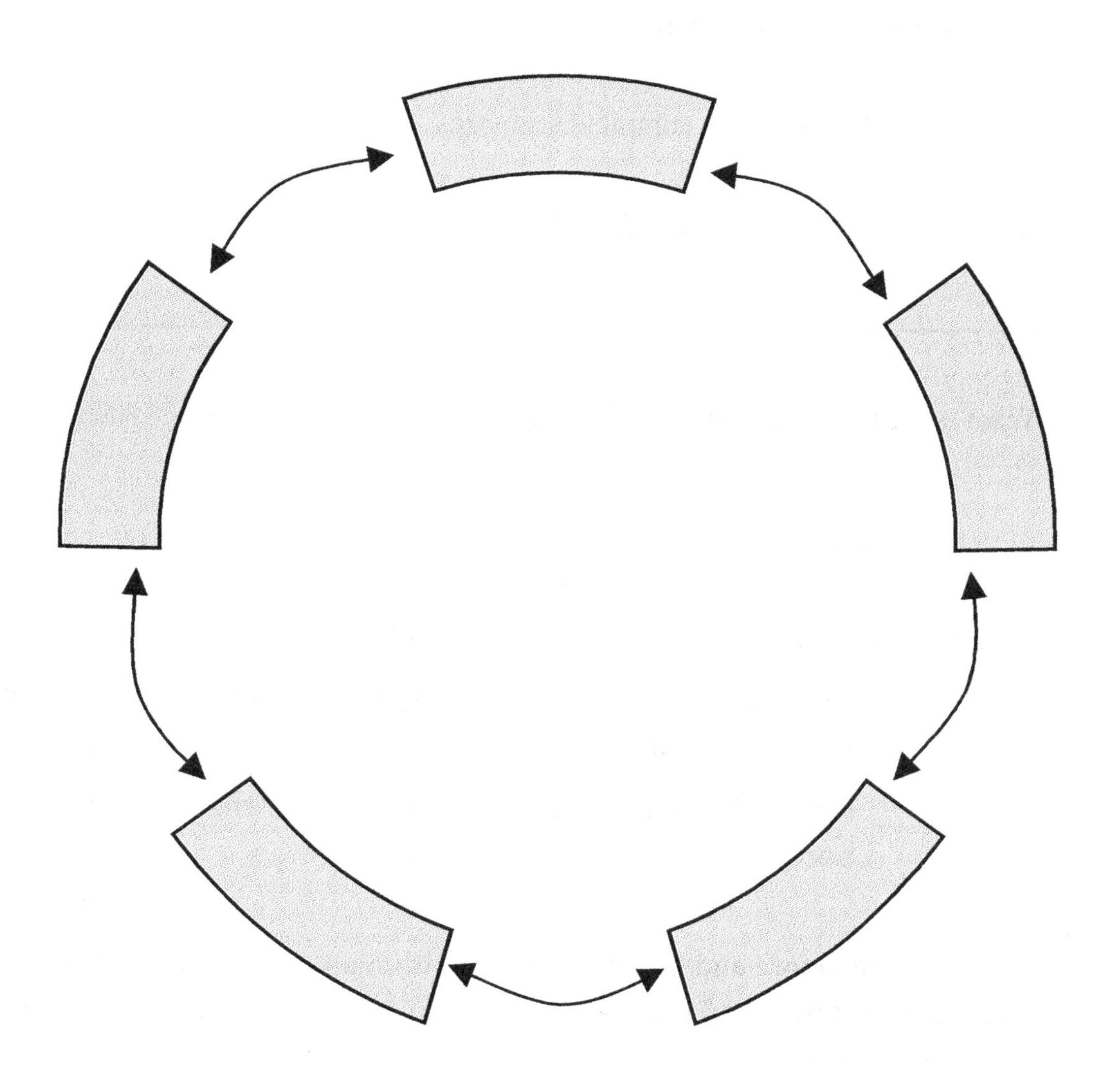

## Lesson #75

Use the following sentences to complete items 1 – 4.

Traci's cat moves through the house, as stealthily as an approaching summer storm. You never see her coming; then all of a sudden, there she is. Purring and pacing near your feet.

1. Underline the simile.

2. List two things being compared in the simile.

   ______________________ and ______________________

3. Draw a line through the sentence fragment; think about what is missing.

4. Rewrite the fragment as a complete sentence.

   ________________________________________________

   ________________________________________________

5. What is the meaning of this symbol? # (Look in the *Help Pages* if you are not sure.)

   ________________________________________________

6. Put a ✓ next to the sentence that states an opinion.

   ____ According to a recent survey, parents will spend more money than they did last year on back-to-school clothing.

   ____ No matter who pays, kids must choose their own clothes because they know what looks cool.

7. **Use a comma before and/or after a quote within a sentence. Example:** "The music was interesting," commented Jamie, "but the dialogue was confusing." (Notice how the commas set off each part so that the meaning is clear.)
   Insert commas.

   "Everyone is present" announced Mrs. Rob "so we can begin."

8. **Remember, capitalize proper nouns and abbreviations that stand for proper nouns. Examples:** Rev., Mr., Ms., Mrs., F (Fahrenheit), C (Celsius)
Underline the sentence that has no errors.

The priest at our parish is father Paul. He works with Deacon Dan and mr. Patrick. I'm pretty sure that Sr. Regina teaches at the school.

9. Most abbreviations begin with a ____________________ and end with a ____________________.

10. Underline the demonstrative. Is it used as a pronoun or an adjective?

Felix enjoyed playing that drum. pronoun adjective

11. Complete the sentence by adding the past perfect form of the verb *bite*.

Terra ____________ ________________ into the bagel before she realized it was made with raisins.

12. Adverbs that tell *when* have to do with time: again, finally, first, later, next, often, then, tomorrow. Use one of these adverbs in a sentence of your own.

_______________________________________________

_______________________________________________

_______________________________________________

# Lesson #76

1. See if you can arrange these words, which are borrowed from the Gaelic language, in the chart below. Use a dictionary if you need help.

blarney trousers galore phony smithereens

| | |
|---|---|
| A) | large quantity; plenty |
| B) | nonsense |
| C) | pants |
| D) | small bits |
| E) | false; fake |

2. Remember, a **cause** tells *why*. Which of these states a cause?

   A) Taking a test makes Bryan very nervous.

   B) So, Bryan studies hard and gets plenty of sleep before he takes a test.

   C) Neither sentence states a cause.

3. Insert commas.

   "Everywhere you look" marveled Elaine "there are dozens of roses."

**Most abbreviations of standard measurement (time, distance, temperature, volume, etc.) use lower case letters and end in a period.**
**Examples:** doz. (dozen) ft. (foot) gal. (gallon) mi. (mile)
Do not use abbreviations for measurement in formal writing. Whenever possible, spell out the number and the unit of measurement.

4. Write the abbreviation for each of the following; use a dictionary if you need help.

   pints ➡ ________ quarts ➡ ________ yards ➡ ________

5. Underline the object pronoun.

   Laurie and I planted her garden and tended it all summer.

6. Underline the word that completes the analogy.

*Crowded* is to *uninhabited* as ______________ is to *colossal.*

miniature fantastic gigantic swarming

7. Complete the sentence by adding the future perfect form of the verb *bite*.

By the end of the evening, mosquitoes __________ ____________

________________ us all!

8 – 12. What are some of your school memories? Write five sentences beginning with "I remember..." Make your sentences about school memories.

______________________________________________

______________________________________________

______________________________________________

______________________________________________

______________________________________________

______________________________________________

______________________

______________________

______________________

______________________

______________________

______________________

# Lesson #77

1. Write the plural form of each of these nouns.

   tooth ➡ ____________ mouse ➡ ____________

| Review | | | |
|---|---|---|---|
| Root | Meaning | Root | Meaning |
| auto- | self | chrono- | time |
| geo- | earth | mono- | one |

2. The right of self-government is ____________.

   binomial autonomy monochrome chronological

3. What is the meaning of this symbol? **$** (Look in the *Help Pages* if you are not sure.)

   ______________________________

4. Cassandra took a long relaxed breath, enjoying the tranquil evening.
   What is the meaning of the underlined word?

   disturbing calm horrific alarming

5. Which sentence is a fact?

   A) Training for a marathon is hard work and takes plenty of discipline.

   B) A marathon may require competitors to run a distance of more than 26 miles.

6. **It is not necessary to use a comma at the end of a quote if there is another punctuation mark. Example:** "Look at all the balloons!" cried Georgie. "Can we get one?"
   Insert quotation marks and end punctuation.

   When will the pizza be ready asked Reyna I'm hungry

7 – 8. Write the meaning of each abbreviated title. **Example:** Mr. ➡ Mister or Master

Rev. ➡ ____________________ Gov. ➡ ____________________

Maj. ➡ ____________________ Atty. ➡ ____________________

9. Choose the correct subject of this sentence.

(Marissa and I / Me and Marissa) will lead the exercises today.

10. **What is the difference between a clause and a phrase? Both can be part of a sentence. A phrase is just a group of words; a clause has a subject and a verb.** Write C next to each clause and P next to each phrase.

_____ beside the nest

_____ since we have eaten

_____ before it starts to rain

**Proof It!** Use two different editing marks to correct errors in each of the following sentences.

11. They're are some precautions you can take you to prevent your dog from getting lost.

SIT

12. Teach your dog commands, like "stay" and "come," and Be sure to check the fents around your yard to make sure it is secure.

# Lesson #78

1. See if you can arrange these words, which are borrowed from the Greek language, in the chart below. Use a dictionary if you need help.

chorus alphabet dinosaur symphony python

| A) | letters representing sounds |
|---|---|
| B) | group that sings or dances |
| C) | terrible lizard |
| D) | large serpent |
| E) | sounding together |

2. Refer to the chart in the previous lesson. What do you think a *chronicle* is?

vegetation water power living things historical account

3. Is the underlined part a **cause** or an **effect**?

Sean stays away from bees because <u>he is allergic to bee stings</u>.

cause effect

4. **Use a comma to separate consecutive words or numbers, when writing a date.**
**Examples:** Tuesday, May 29, 2007 Insert commas.

She got married on Monday January 26 1959.

5. **Abbreviations are not used in formal writing (except for titles).** Use them when addressing an envelope, taking notes, or where space is limited. Which would be appropriate for formal writing?

two dozen eggs 2 doz. eggs

6. Underline the possessive pronoun.

I heard that they're going to give us our refund soon.

7. **A phrase is just a group of words; a clause has a subject and a verb.** Write C next to each clause and P next to each phrase.

____ although you were late

____ after the rain

____ under my teacher's chair

Study the Thompson's Family Tree shown below. Then answer the next five questions.

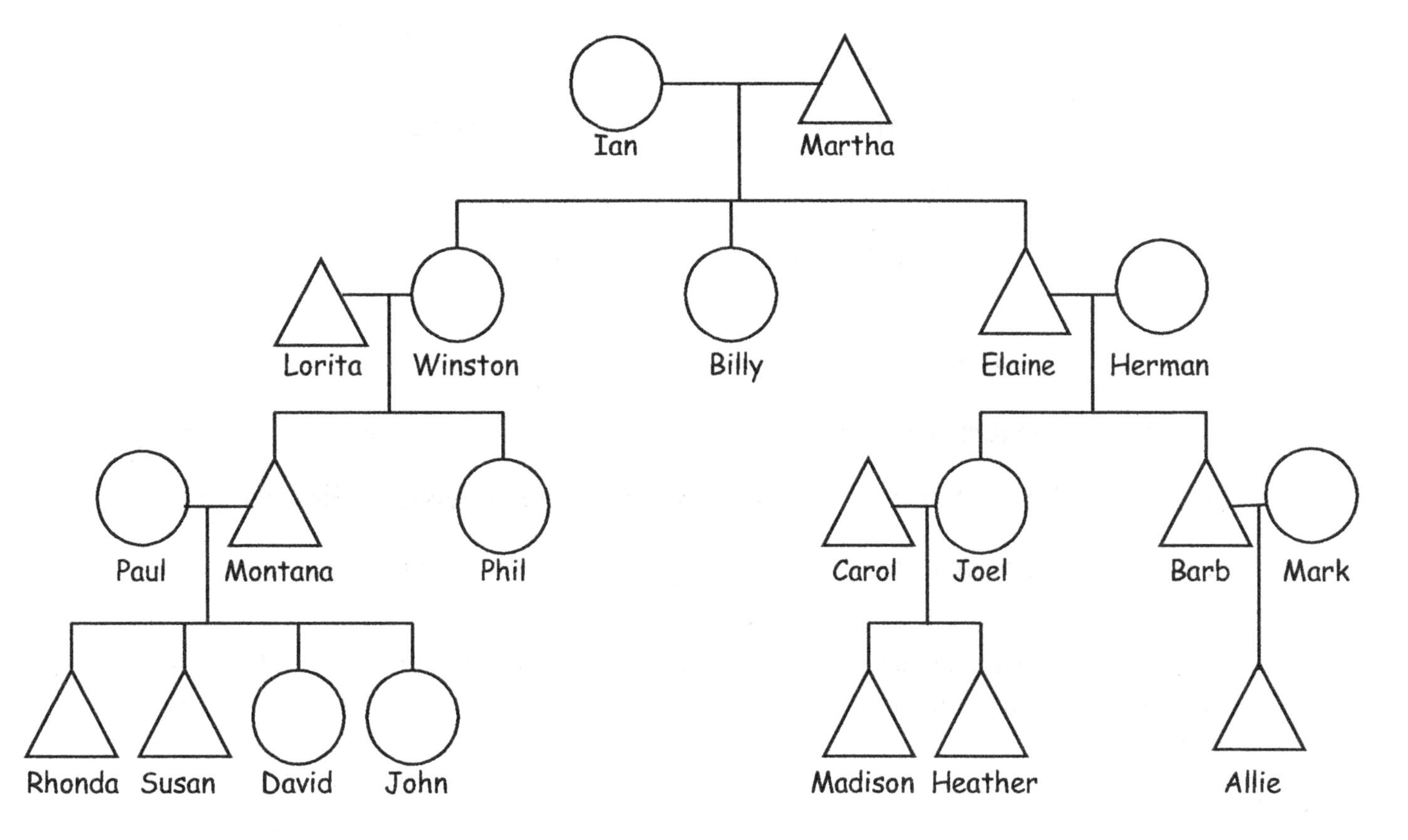


8. How many children do Martha and Ian have? __________

How many grandchildren do they have? __________

9. Who is Montana's mother? ______________________

10. Who is Paul's brother-in-law? ______________________

11. Who are Madison and Heather's parents? ______________________

12. Who is Lorita's father-in-law? ______________________

## Lesson #79

1. Use what you know about roots to complete the sentence. A monodrama is a play written for _______________.

   A) one actor  B) many actors  C) humanity  D) environmentalists

2. What is the meaning of this symbol? % (Look in the *Help Pages* if you are not sure.)

   ___________________________________________

3. Find the meaning and pronunciation of the word *solemn* in a dictionary. Place a ✓ next to any statement that is true.

   ____ Another word for solemn is "serious."

   ____ Solemn is an Olympic sport.

   ____ Solemn rhymes with column.

4. Underline the opinion.

   Many teenagers wear braces to correct dental malformations, and many also wear contact lenses or glasses to perfect their vision. Glasses look great on some people, but most teenagers do not like the look of braces.

5. **If you are not sure of the spelling or meaning of an abbreviation, look in the dictionary**. Find the meaning of this abbreviation in a dictionary and write it on the line.

   hp ➡ ___________________________________________

6. Choose the correct verb.

   I (is / was / be) working late last night.

7. **A phrase is just a group of words; a clause has a subject and a verb.** Write C next to each clause and P next to each phrase.

   ____ as soon as we arrived  ____ if anyone comes

   ____ ever so gently

8. **The verb *lay* means "to put, arrange, or set something down." It is a transitive verb. Example:** Lay those towels on the rack.
Underline the present perfect form of the verb *lay*.

The carpenters have laid this type of flooring many times before.

9. **Homonym Riddle:** This word means "the opposite of right" and is the past tense of *leave*. What is it?

______________________________

10. Why is the letter *C* capitalized in 17°C?

A) *C* stands for "cold"

B) *C* stands for Celsius, which is a proper noun

C) the *C* should not be capitalized

**Proof It!** Rewrite the following sentences, which have been edited.

11. Art Fry and Spencer Silver share the credit for developing those post-it notes.

______________________________

______________________________

12. This very popualar (sp) item is used ~~wide~~ widely in offices and schools.

______________________________

______________________________

______________________________

______________________________

______________________________

## Lesson #80

1. Which is a **cause** and which is an **effect**? Write C or E.

_____As a result of the hurricane warning, _______schools were closed.

2. Add commas where necessary.

On Tuesday September 5 we will return to class, and we'll have another holiday on Monday October 17.

3. **Abbreviations of state names (postal abbreviations) do not end in a period. They are made up of two capital letters.** Match these abbreviations with their state names.

TX CA VT PA

California ➡ _______________ Vermont ➡ _______________

Pennsylvania ➡ _______________ Texas ➡ _______________

4. Decide whether the indefinite pronoun is singular or plural, and choose the other pronoun that agrees.

None of the landscaping (were / was) in need of water.

singular plural

5. Write C next to each clause and P next to each phrase.

____ outside the house ____ whenever the doorbell rings

____ when you are finished

6. Choose the word pair which best completes the analogy. piano : pianist :: __ : __

| | |
|---|---|
| outfielder : coach | doctor : patient |
| voice : singer | violin : orchestra |

7. **The verb *lie* may mean "to recline, stretch out, or lounge." It does not act on anything or anyone else. It is an intransitive verb.**
**Example:** Why don't you lie down on the cot?
Underline the present perfect form of the verb *lie*.

His skin is pink because he has lain around in the sun all day.

8 – 12. Think about a fictional character that you admire or despise. The character can be from a novel, a television program, or a film. Explain why you admire or despise this character in five sentences.

______________________________

______________________________

______________________________

______________________________

______________________________

______________________________

______________________________

______________________________

## Lesson #81

1. **Some nouns keep the same spelling whether they are singular or plural. Examples:** deer, moose, sheep **If you are not sure of the spelling of a plural, use a dictionary to check.** Write the plural form of each noun.

   calf ➡ ____________________ trout ➡ ____________________

   goose ➡ ____________________

2. Words containing *-graph-* or *-gram-* are from the Greek and have to do with writing, drawing, or recording. See if you can match the words in this list with their meanings in the chart below.

   cartography homograph seismograph biography

| | |
|---|---|
| A) | word that is written like another word |
| B) | records movement of the earth |
| C) | drawing maps |
| D) | the story of someone's life |

3. Have you seen this symbol? What does it stand for?

   ____________________________________________

   ____________________________________________

4. Find the word *conspicuous* in a thesaurus or dictionary. Underline its meaning.

   a container of fruit jealous eye-catching

5. Is this statement a fact or an opinion?

   April 24, National Take Our Daughters to Work Day, was created to expose girls to a variety of career options.

   fact opinion

6. Underline the relative pronoun and dependent clause in this sentence.

The recipe that I always use is my grandmother's.

7. Write C next to each clause and P next to each phrase.

____ will be drawing ____ over there ____ as I said

8. Underline the past perfect form of the verb *lay*.

Micah had lain out her clothes and packed her bags the night before her flight.

9. Underline two synonyms.

elated troublesome difficult lonely

10. Is the underlined homograph a verb or a noun?

Please record each person's name next to today's date.

verb noun

11. **Always write a person's exact words within quotation marks. Example:** Donna Ford says, "Smart people, who don't work, eventually fail." Add a comma and quotation marks to this sentence.

My grandmother always said Many hands make light work.

12. **Proof it!** Rewrite the sentence below with correct capitalization and punctuation.

one of Indira Gandhi's famous sayings is you cannot shake hands with a clenched fist.

______________________________________________

______________________________________________

______________________________________________

## Lesson #82

1. What is the plural form of each noun? Use a dictionary if you need help.

   fish ➡ ________________ offspring ➡ ____________________

   sheep ➡ ______________ headquarters ➡ ________________

2. Three of these words are synonyms; cross out the word that does not belong in this list.

   serious hilarious amusing humorous

3. Write C next to the cause and E next to the effect.

   _____Electricity is called a "secondary source" _____because it is derived from other sources like coal, natural gas and nuclear power.

4. **When writing an address, insert a comma between each separate part. Example:** I live at 6963 Park Street, Lakeville, Ohio. Insert commas.

   Bertie sent the package to 1420 East Avenue Austin Texas.

5. Rewrite these names correctly. dr perez and her husband, r j perez

   ____________________________________________________________

6. Choose the correct pronoun. (Hint: Would you say "with they" or "with them?")

   With (who / whom) will you be working?

7. Write C next to each clause and P next to each phrase.

   ____ about the next story ____ although I tried

   ____ everyone eats pizza

8. Underline the <u>future perfect form</u> of the verb *lay*.

   By the year 2010, we will have laid the groundwork for the creation of our new city.

9. Here are some adverbs that tell *where:* inside, outside, upstairs, downstairs, far, forward, here, somewhere. Underline the adverbs.

   Mom said she left her glasses somewhere; I saw them upstairs.

10. Is the demonstrative in this sentence a pronoun or an adjective?

    Why did you say <u>that</u>? pronoun adjective

**Proof It!** Use two editing marks to correct errors in each of the following sentences.

11. did you ever think you might like to have a career working with sharks.

12. Believe it or not, are there are many ocupashuns related to this branch of marine biology.

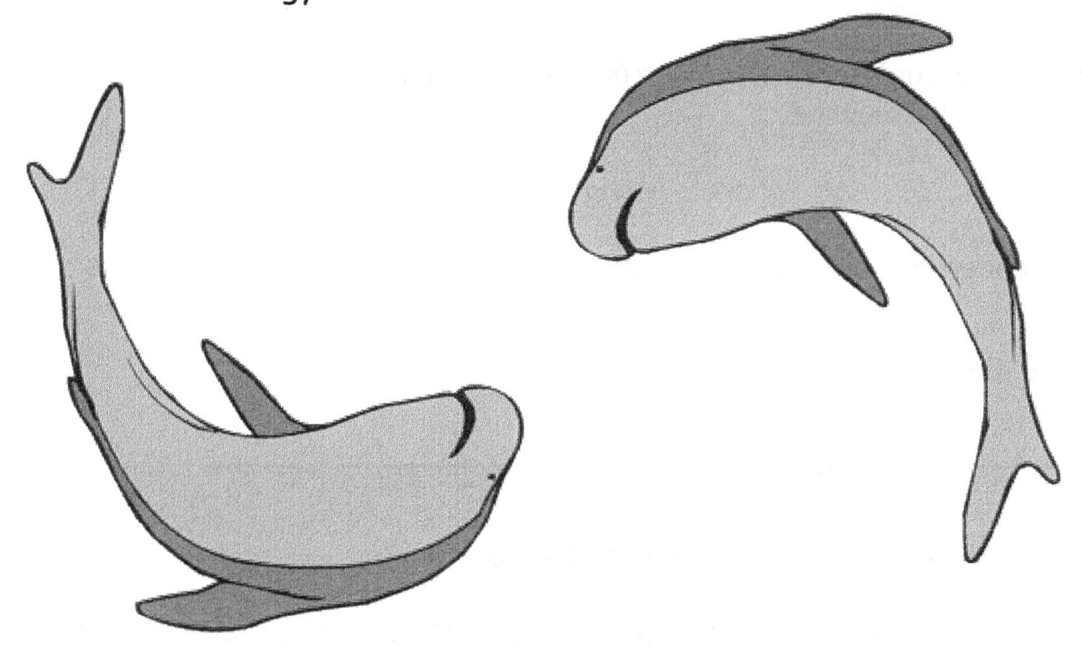

# Lesson #83

1. What is the plural form of each noun? Use a dictionary if you need help.

   species ➧ ________________ barracks ➧ ____________________

   perch ➧ ________________

2. See if you can arrange these words, which are borrowed from the Hebrew language, in the chart below. Use a dictionary if you need help.

   jubilee bedlam kibbutz abacus

| | |
|---|---|
| A) | device for counting |
| B) | joyful time |
| C) | confusion |
| D) | community or group |

3. Take a look at this symbol. What do you think it means?

   ________________________________________

   ________________________________________

4. Find these words in a thesaurus or dictionary. Underline the word that best completes the sentence.

   grave vigorous traitorous

   The cheer leaders use their most ____ cheers when the teams' scores are tied.

5. What is a clause?

   ____________________________________________________________

6. Choose the word that correctly completes the sentence.

   (Its / It's) not too late to plant the strawberries.

7. This sentence states a fact. Rewrite it as an opinion.

Most classrooms have a set of rules, which the teacher expects everyone to follow.

______________________________________________

______________________________________________

8. **Metric abbreviations are not capitalized and do not end in a period.**
**Examples:** m ➡ meter kw ➡ kilowatt l ➡ liter
Remember, do not use abbreviations for measurement in formal writing; it is best to write out the whole word. In which list are all the abbreviations written correctly?

A) 7 Hrs. 20 m. 9° C.
B) 7 hrs. 20 m 9° C
C) 7 hr 20 M 9° C
D) all the lists are correct

9. **Avoid using a pronoun if there is no antecedent. Examples:** We really enjoyed the tour; she was very comical. (This sentence is unclear, since there is no antecedent.) We really enjoyed the tour; the guide was very comical. (This sentence is clear.) Rewrite the following sentence so that it is clear.

Noel doesn't mind going to the class, because she is so nice.

______________________________________________

10. Match each subject with a verb that agrees.

| | |
|---|---|
| It | are |
| We | is |
| I | was |

11. How many main clauses are in this run-on sentence?

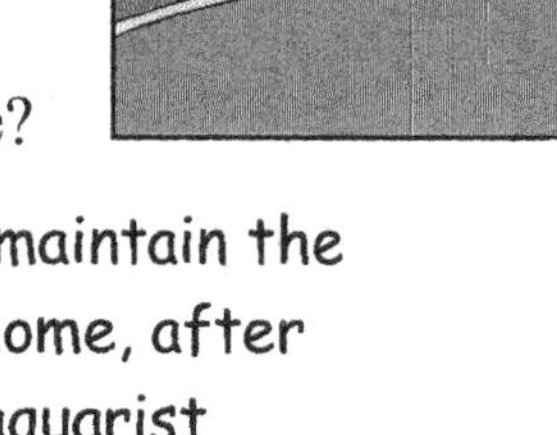

An aquarist works at an aquarium and she must maintain the quality of the animals' water, the tank is their home, after all and the animals must be fed – no wonder an aquarist needs an advanced degree in zoology or marine biology! __________

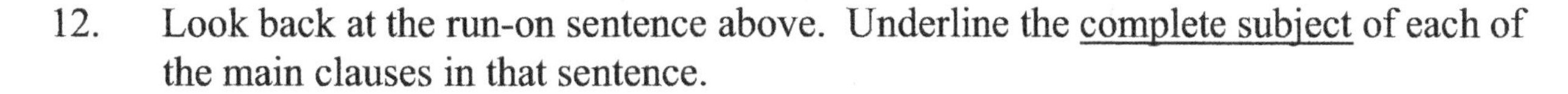

12. Look back at the run-on sentence above. Underline the complete subject of each of the main clauses in that sentence.

# Lesson #84

1. Write C next to the cause and E next to the effect.

   ____Paullina's baby sister has asthma ____so they can't have a dog or a cat in the house. ____Since Paullina asked for a pet, ____her parents got her a parakeet for her birthday.

2. **Use a comma after the greeting and the closing in a friendly letter.**
   **Examples:** Dear Regis, To Whom This May Concern, Sincerely yours,

   **Use a colon after the greeting in a formal or business letter; use a comma after the closing. Examples:** Dear Mr. Phillips: Sincerely,

   Insert punctuation to make this writing correct.

   Dear Mr. Kent

   We have received your letter of complaint. Your concern will be discussed at our next business meeting.

   Sincerely

   David Wills

3. Write the meanings of the abbreviations.

   Bldg. ➡ ____________________ Apt. ➡ ____________________

   Ave. ➡ ____________________

4. Evaluate this sentence. Him and me have been best friends since kindergarten.

   A) sentence is correct as is

   B) verbs do not agree with subject

   C) pronouns case is incorrect

5. Complete the analogy. *Acting* is to *actor* as *cooking* is to _____.

   waiter designer chef order

6. What is a phrase?

______________________________________________

7. Choose the verbs that agree with the subjects of these sentences.

The African Union (was / were) established in 2002.

There (is / are) 53 countries in the African Union.

8 – 12. What do you think is the most difficult thing about being a boy or girl your age? List at least five things or write a short paragraph.

______________________________________________

______________________________________________

______________________________________________

______________________________________________

______________________________________________

______________________________________________

______________________________________________

______________________________________________

______________________________________________

______________________________________________

## Lesson #85

1. Have you seen this symbol? What does it stand for?

 ________________________________________

 ________________________________________

2. Remember, the denotation of a word is its literal meaning. What is the denotation of the word *lame* in this sentence?

 Gregory's dog is lame because it was hit by a car.

 A) crippled B) silly C) sorry D) inadequate

3. Many environmentalists are concerned about global warming. They believe that future generations will bear the burden of this calamity. Which of these is not a synonym for *calamity*?

 A) cataclysm B) catastrophe C) disaster D) circumstance

4. The prefix *amphi-* means "both." Which word means "able to live on both land and water?"

 diametric metamorphic amphibious chronological

5. Choose the possessive pronoun that correctly completes the sentence.

 The house with the red roof is (our / ours).

6 – 12. The following paragraph may contain some errors. Evaluate the writing, and complete the checklist that follows.

Decomposers are important to us because they are the organisms that cause decay. Some common decomposers are flies, beetles, centipedes, earthworms and bacteria. All types of waste: garbage, fallen leaves, rotting trees, and dead animals. Sometimes people just throw garbage on the ground. We used to call them "litterbugs." These organic materials would never rot or disintegrate without the help of decomposers. Instead of allowing refuse to pile up, decomposers breaks down organic waste. It then becomes nutrient-rich soil for growing plants.

6. Is there a topic sentence? _____ Yes _____ No

If there is a clear topic sentence, underline it. If not, write a suitable topic sentence below.

_______________________________________________

_______________________________________________

7. Do all of the details support the main idea? _____ Yes _____ No
If not, draw a line through any sentences that are irrelevant.

8. Does each sentence have an end mark? _____ Yes _____ No
If not, make corrections, using the editing marks.

9. Does each sentence have subject-verb agreement? _____ Yes _____ No
If not, cross out the incorrect verb; add the correct verb, using the editing mark for "add something."

10. Does each sentence begin with a capital letter? _____ Yes _____ No
If not, make corrections, using the editing marks.

11 – 12. Does every sentence express a complete thought? _____ Yes _____ No

If there are any fragments, put brackets [ ] around them. Rewrite a fragment as a complete sentence here.

_______________________________

_______________________________

_______________________________

_______________________________

_______________________________

_______________________________

## Lesson #86

1. Choose the word that completes this analogy.

   *Microscope* is to *biologist* as *stethoscope* is to ______________

   physician    teacher    lawyer    economist

2. Choose the correct homophones.

   The (reel / real) on my fishing (pole / poll) is locked.

3. The Latin root *-port-* means "carry." Many words that have to do with travel contain this root. Circle the words that probably come from the Latin root *-port-*.

   transportation    porous    airport    seaport

4. Look at this section from the index of a mathematics text. Use it to answer the next three questions.

   **Circle,** 256-257
   - area, 258
   - center, 260
   - central angles, 249
   - chord, 257
   - circumference, 252
   - diameter, 258
   - graphs, 199-203
   - parts of, 257
   - pi, 187, 234
   - radius, 259
   - tangent, 257

   A) On what page would you find the formula for the area of a circle?

   ______________

   B) On what pages is the term *pi* mentioned?

   ______________

   C) Where, in the book, would you find the definition of a circle?

   ______________

5. Underline the sentence which states a fact.

   Mount Everest, the highest mountain in the world, is in the Himalayas, which stretch through Nepal and Tibet. Only the most capable and resolute climbers dare to climb Mount Everest.

6. Underline the complete subject.

Five really great picnic foods can fit into this basket.

7. Complete the sentence with a form of the verb *be* that agrees with the subject.

_______________ there really a "Loch Ness Monster" or not?

8. A man named J. P. Morgan once said, "You can't unscramble eggs." This saying is like all of the following, except which?

A) You can't put the toothpaste back in the tube.

B) Some processes are irreversible.

C) You can't judge a book by its cover.

D) What's done is done.

9 – 12. J. P. Morgan was an immensely wealthy man, who invested in twentieth century technology and made sizeable donations to museums, universities and hospitals. Read another quote from J. P. Morgan:

"Go as far as you can see; when you get there, you'll be able to see farther."

Write at least five sentences about what this quote means to you.

_______________________________________________

_______________________________________________

_______________________________________________

_______________________________________________

_______________________________________________

_______________________________________________

_______________________________________________

_______________________________________________

## Lesson #87

1. Three of these words are synonyms. Cross out the word that doesn't belong.

   pungent sharp floral bitter

2. Frogs, toads, newts, and salamanders are some of the common amphibians found in North America. The underlined word refers to ________.

   A) animals of the tundra
   B) animals that live both on land and in water
   C) very small animals
   D) extinct animals

3. What does this symbol stand for? ____________________

   ______________________________________________

4. Write the word with its suffix. deploy + -ing ➡ ____________________

5. Are you *adamant* about anything in particular? Find the meaning of *adamant* in a dictionary or thesaurus, and write a synonym for it here.

   ____________________

6. **A run-on sentence has too many main clauses or lacks proper punctuation.** Put a ⊙ in the following example to show where the first sentence should end.

   If our soccer team wins one more game, we will qualify for the state finals that means we will be taking a bus trip to Harrisburg.

7. See if you can arrange these words, which are borrowed from the Japanese language, in the chart below. Use a dictionary if you need help.

   sushi futon karaoke ninja karate

| | |
|---|---|
| A) | singing to pre-recorded music |
| B) | warrior |
| C) | raw fish |
| D) | combat without weapons |
| E) | couch-bed |

Read the following paragraph before you complete items 8 – 11.

When an author writes an original piece of work, that person owns what she or he has written. No one has the right to copy another writer's work without that author's permission. Copying another person's work without permission is called **plagiarism**. Plagiarism is both illegal and against school rules.

You will be required to write reports and research papers for school. When you are doing research at the library or on the internet, it is okay to use information that you find. But you must put the information into your own words, and you need to give credit to the writer or "source." You can give credit by listing the name(s) of authors and their book titles in your bibliography. A bibliography is a list of books and other sources. Look in the *Help Pages* for more information about how to set up a bibliography.

8 – 9 Underline a complex sentence in the first paragraph and a compound sentence in the second paragraph.

10. What is plagiarism? ______________________________

______________________________________________

______________________________________________

11. What can you do to avoid plagiarism?

A) List your sources in a bibliography.
C) Write information in your own words.
B) Never copy someone else's work.
D) all of these

12. Why is the letter *E* capitalized in this address? 207 E. Wilber St.

A) it is part of the street name, which is a proper noun
B) the word east should always be capitalized
C) it is an error

## Lesson #88

1. Think about the meaning of the root *-port-*. What does a *porter* do?

| | |
|---|---|
| studies living things | carries things |
| measures temperature | lives in water |

2. Find the meaning of the word *venture* in a dictionary. Place a ✓ next to the statement that is true.

   ____ A venture is a scavenger.

   ____ A venture may be risky.

   ____ A venture is a type of car.

Read each sentence, and label it: simple, compound, or complex. Check the *Help Pages* if you get stuck.

3. My best memory is the day we saw our new house. ____________________

4. There are four kids in my family, so we had to share bedrooms in the old apartment. ____________________

5. There was neither a playground nor any grass near the apartment complex. ____________________

6. In our new house each kid would have his own room, and we would have a big yard in the back of the house. ____________________

7. **In most cases, place commas and end marks inside quotation marks.** Think of quotation marks as the "frame" around phrases or complete sentences. **Example:** "Is everyone ready?" Which is correct?

| | |
|---|---|
| A) "Let's go!" cried Miguel. | C) "Let's go cried Miguel!" |
| B) "Let's go"! cried Miguel. | D) "Let's go" cried Miguel. |

8. Complete the sentence by adding the present perfect form of the verb *deal*.

   Mr. Lucas ____________ ______________ with this issue for many years.

9. **Adverbs modify verbs, adjectives, or other adverbs. They tell: *how, when, where*, or *to what extent*.** What word does the adverb in this sentence modify?

Dr. Benjamin explained the problem *thoroughly*. ________________

10 – 12. Write a three-sentence story. Tell about your day in just three sentences. Write one of each type of sentence: simple, complex, and compound.

______________________________________________

______________________________________________

______________________________________________

______________________________________________

______________________________________________

______________________________________________

## Lesson #89

1. Is the homograph a verb, a noun, or an adjective?

   I would like to present our guest speaker, Dr. Marshal.

   verb noun adjective

2. Circle the words that probably come from the Latin root *-port-*.

   passport pothole heliport papyrus portage

3. Write the meaning (in your own words) of each of the words you circled above.

   ______________________________

   ______________________________

   ______________________________

4. Look in the *Help Pages* to find the meaning of this symbol. ® Write the meaning here.

   ______________________________

5. Write the word with its suffix.

   prey + -ing ➡ ____________ prey + -ed ➡ ____________

6. **A subordinate (dependent) clause has a subject and a verb, but it does not express a complete thought. A subordinate clause is used with a main clause to make a complete sentence.** Which of these is a subordinate clause?

   ____I feel much better ____now that we talked about this.

7. Choose the correct verb.

   Elena and you (was / were) supposed to bring dessert.

8. Complete the sentence by adding the past perfect form of the verb *deal*.

I ____________ _______________ the cards before I noticed how many players there were.

9. **When writing a dialogue, put the speaker's words in quotes and begin a new paragraph each time a different person is speaking.**

**Example:**

"Knock, knock."
"Who's there?"
"Woo."
"Woo, who?"
"Don't get so excited. It's just a knock-knock joke!"

Write your own knock-knock joke below. Use quotation marks and other punctuation correctly.

_______________________________________________

_______________________________________________

_______________________________________________

_______________________________________________

_______________________________________________

10. **An adjective often becomes an adverb by adding –*ly*. Example:** A beautiful flower blooms beautifully. Write the adverb and the adjective.

The __________ little bird sang _______________. (sweet)

Read the following sentence and then complete items 11 and 12.

Yesterday I wasn't feeling well, but after a good night's sleep I feel as right as rain!
A. B. C.

11. Which of the underlined parts is not a clause? __________

12. Which of the underlined parts includes a simile? __________

## Lesson #90

1. Which pair of words completes this analogy? public : private :: ____ : ____

   night : evening　　　open : closed

   secretive : personal　　　national : government

2. The prefix *dia-* means "across."

   A ________ line runs across a surface.

   circumference　　diagonal　　informational　　portable

3. **An independent (main) clause has a subject and a verb; it can stand alone as a complete sentence.** Which of these is an independent clause?

   ____ While you are here ____ I would like to show you the garden.

4. **Use quotation marks to signify the title of a short work, such as a poem, song, short story, or book chapter. Example:** We read Ken Nesbitt's funny poem, "Levitating Lester," and we practiced singing "The Star-Spangled Banner." Insert quotation marks.

   Daisha wrote a song called, Summer Sun and a poem entitled, All That.

5. Complete the sentence by adding the future perfect form of the verb *deal.*

   By the end of the game, everyone __________ __________ __________ at least one hand.

Read these paragraphs and use them to complete the next five items.

When doing research, you must be careful not to **plagiarize**. How can you use information from a book, encyclopedia, or the internet if it is illegal to copy it? Here are some ways to help you avoid plagiarism while you are doing research. First, look for information in books, magazines, newspapers, or on a website. The more places you look, the better your research will be. When you find information that you want to use, write down the name of the author, the book title, the publisher, and year of publication. If it is a website, you may find instructions called "citing this page." If not, write down the web address for that page. Then take careful notes. Never download or copy what you find in books, magazines, or online to add to a report.

When you are ready to write your report, look at your notes. Put the information in your own words, sentences, and paragraphs. Include the most important facts. If you want to add your opinion, put it in a separate paragraph. Finally, be sure to write a complete bibliography. List all the sources you used. Also, you may want to list other sources that you consulted, but did not use for this report. Your teacher or your school will have a certain format to follow, but the author's name will always be included.

For items 6 – 10 write T for true or F for false next to each statement.

6. ____ One way to avoid plagiarism is to put information in my own words.

7. ____ A bibliography should include the names of authors, as well as titles, and publishers of the books, articles, and other information used in a report.

8. ____ It is okay to print a page off an internet website and include it in a school report.

9. ____ It is illegal to use what I have learned from a book, encyclopedia, or the internet in a school report.

10. ____ When writing a report or research paper, it is a good idea to make use of as many sources as possible.

11 – 12. **Remember, a complex sentence contains a main clause and a dependent clause, joined by a subordinating conjunction**. Use the information below to write two complex sentences. Choose two clauses and a subordinating conjunction for each sentence.

Subordinating Conjunctions ➡ after, when, even though, before, unless

Clauses ➡ the rain stopped, everyone got soaked, the water began to rise, people ran for cover, the thunder and lightening began, the sky darkened, they had umbrellas

______________________________________________

______________________________________________

______________________________________________

______________________________________________

## Lesson #91

1. Are any of these plurals misspelled? Use a dictionary to check. Then write any misspelled words correctly.

   dice familys sheaf's lice

   ______________________________

2. Underline two antonyms in this sentence.

   Although the cinematography was surprising, the plot was quite predictable.

3. Damien was told to bring a portfolio of his work to the interview. Based on what you know about prefixes, a *portfolio* is probably what?

   A) a type of interview
   B) something you carry
   C) a resume
   D) a set of test results

4. What is the meaning of this symbol? ______________________________

   ______________________________

5. Look in a dictionary or thesaurus and find a better word for *stupid*. Write your word on the line.

   ______________________________

6. Which of these is an independent clause?

   ____ Brady ran out of the house ____like he was being chased by a tiger!

7. Does the sentence in item six use a simile or a metaphor?

   simile metaphor

8. **Use quotation marks to show the definition of a word. Example:** The term *de jour* means "of the day." Insert quotation marks.

   The word *quintessential* means exemplary.

9. Rewrite this fact as an opinion.

According to the weather forecast, there is a 30 percent chance of rain this afternoon.

______________________________________________

______________________________________________

10. Underline the correct verb.

She and I (play / plays) the duet together.

11. See if you can arrange these words, which are borrowed from the Norwegian and Polish languages, in the chart below. Use a dictionary if you need help.

dollop slalom fjord horde

| | |
|---|---|
| A) | large group |
| B) | long, narrow inlet |
| C) | small amount |
| D) | sloping track |

12. Read this run-on sentence. Then rewrite it correctly, by using conjunctions, arranging clauses, and breaking the run-on down into smaller sentences.

In late August of 2005, there was a devastating hurricane which destroyed much of New Orleans and it was called Hurricane Katrina and many people died and others lost their homes and it took years to rebuild the city and some families left the area and never returned.

______________________________________________

______________________________________________

______________________________________________

______________________________________________

## Lesson #92

1. Make these nouns plural.

   knife ➡ ___________ self ➡ ___________ elf ➡ ___________

2. An instrument that reads and records temperatures is a ______.

   A) monogram B) portfolio C) spectacle D) thermograph

3. What is a subordinate clause?

   A) A clause that is dependent upon the main clause.

   B) A group of words that has a subject and predicate but does not express a complete thought.

   C) A clause used with a main clause to make a sentence.

   D) all of these

4. Insert the proper punctuation.

   The term *RSVP* means répondez s'il vous plait

5. Many words can be used as either adverbs or prepositions. **Remember, adverbs modify other words; prepositions are found at the beginning of a prepositional phrase**. What part of speech are these words?

   above down near beside under off

   A) adverbs

   B) prepositions

   C) It depends on how the word is used in a sentence.

6. Remember, *good* is an adjective, so it modifies a noun; *well* is an adverb, so it modifies a verb. Write *good* or *well* to complete each sentence.

   Please rinse the dishes really ______________. It's a ______________ idea to let them air dry.

7. Add the proper punctuation to this interjection.

   Wow This is great

8. Choose the correct pronoun.

(He / They) were able to reschedule the game.

9. Read each cause-effect statement below. Then, underline the part of each sentence that states the cause.

Jason loves to play video games, so he often visits Games 'n More, a local video rental store. Since renting or buying video games can be expensive, Jason has gotten a job at Games 'n More. Jason is a great sales representative because he knows a lot about the most popular games for kids his age.

10. Underline the words that should be capitalized.

two oz. attorney general Davis grandma and her mother

11. Write the meaning of the underlined word.

They'll be here any minute! ______________________

12. **Proof It!** What is wrong with this sentence? How would you fix it?

Nolan did really good on his report card this year in fact, he may even be the class valedictorian.

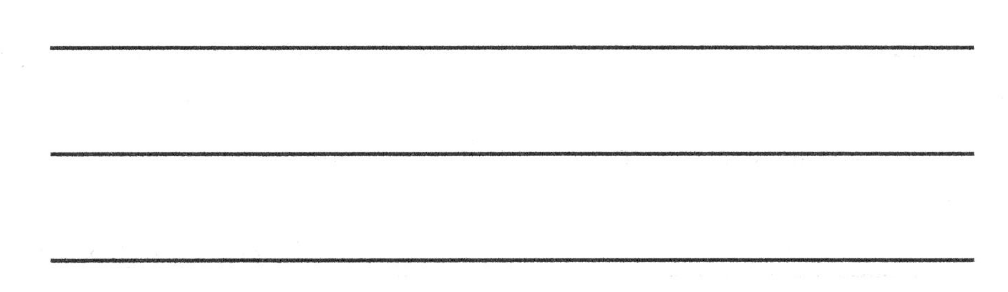

## Lesson #93

1. Make these nouns plural.

   wallaby ➡ __________ topaz ➡ __________ trolley ➡ __________

2. **Homonym Riddle:** This word means "the soft feathers of a young bird" or "going lower." What is it?

   ______________________

3. What does this symbol mean? © Look in the *Help Pages*, and write the meaning here.

   ______________________________________________

4. **An adverb modifies a verb, adjective, or other adverb.** Choose the correct word.

   The entire school of fish moves so (quick / quickly) through the water.

5. Which of these is a subordinate clause?

   ___As soon as Martin graduates from high school ____he will go to college.

6. Rewrite these sentences with proper punctuation and capitalization.

   Did you know that today is Roald Dahl's birthday asked Dina

   ______________________________________________

   yes answered Larry he wrote charlie and the chocolate factory

   ______________________________________________

7. Complete the sentence by adding the present perfect form of the verb *feel*.

   Nora ____________ ________________ a little tired all day.

8. Underline the indefinite pronoun, and choose the verb that agrees.

Everything (was / were) clearer after the storm.

Let's look at another way to avoid plagiarism. Sometimes you will want to copy a person's exact words or some information that you can not restate in your own words. If you do copy someone's words, copy them exactly. Always put quotation marks around the exact phrase. Be sure to include the name of the person who said or wrote the words. You should never copy long passages, but short quotes are okay. Here is an **example.** Thomas Edison once said, "We haven't failed. We now know a thousand things that won't work, so we are much closer to finding what will."

9. Put a ✓ next to each phrase that makes the following statement true.

In order to avoid plagiarism, a student should

____ properly cite all sources.

____ hand in downloaded information from the internet.

____ put quotation marks around a person's exact words.

____ never copy somebody else's writing.

10. Which pair of words completes this analogy? national : international :: ____ : ____

prepared : unprepared | beauty : beautiful

continental : intercontinental | oceanic : transoceanic

11 – 12. **Proof It!** These sentences have been edited. Rewrite them correctly.

One of my ~~most~~ favorite characters is the big bad Wolf from the fairy tale, "Little Red Riding Hood."

______________________________________________

______________________________________________

I think ~~he~~ (the wolf) was really clever and ~~generous~~ (creative); he just got a bad rap in the /Story.

______________________________________________

______________________________________________

## Lesson #94

1. Choose the word that completes this analogy.

   *Tireless* is to *weary* as *energetic* is to _______.

   exhausted bouncy emotional lively

2. Sort this list of adjectives. Write each word next to its synonym.

   pleased, nervous, joyful, fatigued, exhausted, worried, elated, sleepy, fretful

   anxious ➡ ____________________

   weary ➡ ____________________

   happy ➡ ____________________

3. Do you tend to be more *voluble* or more *reticent*? Choose the word that you think fits you best and then find its meaning in a dictionary or thesaurus. Write the meaning of the word you chose here.

   ____________ ➡ ____________________

4. What is an independent clause?

   ____________________

5. Insert proper punctuation.

   For homework please read the chapter entitled Places to Visit

6. Complete the sentence by adding the past perfect form of the verb *feel*.

   I __________ __________ unsure of the number, so I checked the book again.

7. Choose the correct word to modify the adjective.

   She chose a (bright / brightly) colored scarf to complete her outfit.

8. **The initials R.S.V.P. (or RSVP) stand for a French expression: "répondez s'il vous plait." This expression means "please respond."** If you receive an invitation with the initials R.S.V.P. it means your host needs to know whether or not you will be able to attend, so be sure to reply. Match these other French words with their meanings.

memoir faux pas ballet portrait

| | |
|---|---|
| A) | painting or photo |
| B) | little dance |
| C) | memory |
| D) | false step (mistake) |

9. Underline the metaphor in this sentence.

Tricia's room was a blizzard of down feathers by the time she broke up the wild pillow fight between little Jamaal and Henry.

10. **For words that end in consonant *-y*, change the *-y* to *-i* when adding *–es*. Examples:** story ➡ stories hurry ➡ hurries Make these nouns plural.

pony ➡ ____________________ mercy ➡ ________________________

**Proof It!** Use two editing marks to correct errors in each of the following sentences.

11. Alexis invented a sandwich made with hole wheat bread, peanut butter, marshmallow spread, and sliced Bananas.

12. she likes to wash it down with ice-cold glass of milk.

## Lesson #95

1. What does this symbol mean? List three places where you might expect to see this symbol.

____________________________________________

____________________________________________

2. **Add –*es* to words ending in s, x, ch, or sh. Examples:** push ➡ pushes switch ➡ switches Make these nouns plural.

church ➡ __________ fox ➡ __________ brush ➡ __________

3. Write C next to each clause and P next to each phrase.

___ down the slide ___ that was too difficult ___ will have studied

4. Insert end marks and quotation marks.

Did you hear about that new little diner in outer space

No, what about it

The food isn't bad, but there's just no atmosphere

5. Write an F if the statement is a fact; write O if it is an opinion.

___ Benjamin Franklin has been called a genius due to his many inventions: the lightening rod, bifocal lenses, the odometer, and the Franklin stove.

___ Franklin was a mastermind, who used his talents to make life better for other people.

6. Complete the sentence by adding the future perfect form of the verb *feel*.

By the end of the year, our state __________ __________

__________ the ill-effects of the budget reduction.

7. Circle the antecedent of the relative pronoun in this sentence.

The classmate to whom you sent an invitation called yesterday.

8. Put a ✓ next to any phrase that will make the sentence true.

In order to avoid plagiarism, never turn in something that...

____ you copied from a book.

____ is not your own work.

____ you downloaded from the internet.

9. What do the initials *R.S.V.P.* (or *RSVP*) tell you to do?

_______________________________________________

10. **The object of a preposition comes at the end of a prepositional phrase.**
**Example:** Lena cried when she dropped her ice cream *onto the ground.*
Underline the object of the preposition.

We were amazed that the deer were strong enough to leap *over the fence.*

11 – 12. **Proof It!** These sentences have been edited. Rewrite them correctly.

On a dreary winter's night, late ^in the month of January, a (beautyful) sp

baby girl was born ⊙

_______________________________________________

_______________________________________________

this amazing child was called Grace because she was the answer to

her Grandmother's prayers.

_______________________________________________

_______________________________________________

# Lesson #96

1. Write C next to each clause and P next to each phrase.

 ____ now that Sheila is here ____ where she was ____making some dinner

2. Insert a comma, an end mark, and quotation marks.

 The Star-Spangled Banner was written by Francis Scott Key on September 13 1814

3. Study the definitions and choose the correct homophone to complete each sentence.

 strait ➡ (*noun*) a narrow body of water

 straight ➡ (*adjective*) not curved

 The sailors navigated the ship (straight / Strait) through the Bering (straight / Strait).

4. List the four demonstrative pronouns.

 ____________ ____________ ____________ ____________

5. Which is a pair of correlative conjunctions will best complete the sentence?

 Marianna wants to be an interpreter, so she studies ___ Spanish ___ French.

 either/or both/and neither/nor not/but

**Proof It!** Use two editing marks to correct errors in each of the following sentences.

6. On labor Day they're is always an exciting parade down Magnolia Street.

7. Afterwards, the Civic Club sponsors colossal picnic at the at main pavilion in Lawrence Park.

Read the following paragraph and use the information to answer questions 8 through 12.

Seasonal affective disorder or SAD is a condition which causes people to feel tired and gloomy during certain seasons of the year, especially winter. The syndrome is called "seasonal" because the depression seems to go away, once the season passes. No one knows for sure what causes SAD, but some people think it has to do with the limited amount of sunlight during the winter months or the change in temperatures. Seasonal affective disorder seems to affect adults more often than children, and people in the northern hemisphere suffer more from SAD than people in the southern hemisphere. There are some medical treatments available for SAD, but no single cure has worked for everyone afflicted with the ailment. Source: www.DiscoveryHealth.com

8. What is the acronym for seasonal affective disorder? ______________________

9. Why do people think that seasonal affective disorder may be caused by a lack of sunlight?

A) SAD affects people mostly during winter.

B) More women than men are diagnosed with SAD.

C) SAD affects adults more often than children.

D) all of these

10. Write an F if the statement is a fact; write O if it is an opinion.

____ Probably the best treatment for SAD is to wait it out, since the condition only occurs during winter.

____ There are some treatments for SAD, but the treatments do not work for everyone.

____ The winter months are hard on everyone because of the cold and darkness.

11. Three of these words are synonyms; cross out the word that does not belong.

disease diagnosis syndrome condition

12. Write C for cause and E for effect.

____The syndrome is called "seasonal" ____because the depression seems to go away, once the season passes.

## Lesson #97

1. Complete the analogy. Use a dictionary if you need help.

   *Convenient* is to *inconvenient* as *stationary* is to ____.

   ambulatory easy problematic immobile

2. **An acronym is a word formed from the initials in a phrase or title. Example:** ASAP ➡ "as soon as possible" Look in a dictionary. Find and write the meaning of this acronym.

   OPEC ➡ ______________________________

3. Rewrite these sentences and fragments to make one complete sentence.

   I rode the roller coasters. Not the Jaguar. But all the other ones. And I had a blast!

   ______________________________

   ______________________________

4. What is the subject of the sentence you wrote in the item above? ________

5. Put a ✓ next to the sentence that states an opinion.

   ____ In 1935, Mary McLeod Bethune organized the National Council of Negro Women.

   ____ This was a defining moment in American history.

6. **Remember, an adverb phrase tells *how*, *when*, *where*, or *why*.** Underline the adverb phrase that modifies the verb *published.*

   Abolitionists published newspapers throughout the North.

7. Use a dictionary or thesaurus to choose a synonym for the underlined word.

   Felicia was aggravated by the <u>incessant</u> drilling of a woodpecker outside her window.

   provoked irritating continual piercing

8. Read the sentence, and match the underlined words with their usage listed below.

On May 3, 1952 two pilots, Joseph Fletcher and William Benedict, landed an aircraft at the North Pole.

| ____________ | ____________ | ____________ | ____________ |
|---|---|---|---|
| subject | action verb | adjective | direct object |

9. Place commas where they are needed in this sentence.

Tatiana was an excellent writer speaker and leader so it was she who was voted captain of the debate team.

10. Use two editing marks to show what is missing in this sentence.

The toy trains were on shelf

11. This sentence has been edited. Write it correctly.

My Dad is ^ engineer at your Goddard Space flight center.
an

___________________________________________________________

12. See if you can arrange these words, which are borrowed from the Spanish language, in the chart below.

cargo renegade alligator mustang tornado

| Common Words with Spanish Origins | | |
|---|---|---|
| English Word | Spanish Word | Original Meaning |
| A) | tronada | thunderstorm |
| B) | renegado | deserter or outlaw |
| C) | mestengo | ownerless, a stray animal |
| D) | el lagarto | the lizard |
| E) | cargar | to load |

# Lesson #98

1. **Notorious or Famous?** Both of these words mean "well-known." But the word *notorious* has an unfavorable connotation (a *notorious* villain), whereas the word *famous* has a positive connotation (a *famous* writer). Decide which word – *notorious* or *famous* – has the most appropriate connotation for each sentence.

   Two (notorious / famous) criminals of the twentieth century were Bonnie Parker and Clyde Barrow. The (notorious / famous) film, *Bonnie and Clyde,* was released in 1967, and it became one of the most popular films of all time.

2. Underline two synonyms in this sentence.

   Julia will nudge the puppy to get him to push open the door.

3. Underline the correct homophones.

   Dora (whiled / wild) away her free time watching (whiled / wild) butterflies.

4. The prefix *anti-* means "against or opposite." Match each word with its meaning.

| | |
|---|---|
| antisocial | works against poison or disease |
| antifungal | unwilling to socialize |
| antidote | works against a fungus |

5. Have you seen this symbol? What does it stand for?

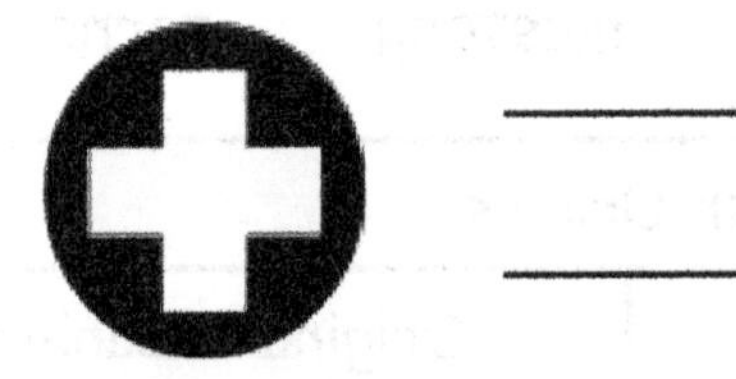

   ______________________________

   ______________________________

6. Make these nouns plural.

   forty ➡ ____________  sixty ➡ ____________

7. **Use a colon before listing items, but only after an independent clause.**
   **Example:** I have lived in five cities: Akron, Mesa, Tulsa, Miami, and Atlanta. (The independent clause can stand alone.) Is the colon used correctly in the following sentence?

   Regina packed everything: blankets, cooler, and camping supplies.  Yes  No

8. **What is the difference between a clause and a sentence? Both contain a subject and a predicate, but a dependent clause does not express a complete thought.** Put a ✓ next to each dependent clause. (Hint: look for subordinate conjunctions.)

_____ as long as you are home by dark

_____ it's the best playground

_____ unless we run out of pizza

9 – 12. What are some of your best "excuses?" Make a list below. Some examples are given.

- "My alarm clock just keeps blinking 12:00. That's why I'm always late."
- "I did my writing assignment, but it was so good that I decided to submit it to a magazine publisher. I'll get you a copy of the first issue."
- "It's not that I forgot to feed the dog; I just felt that a day of fasting would be good for him."

______________________________

______________________________

______________________________

______________________________

______________________________

______________________________

______________________________

______________________________

______________________________

______________________________

______________________________

## Lesson #99

1. Which of the following is an antonym for the word *laborious*?

   arduous difficult backbreaking effortless

2. Is the homograph a verb, a noun, or an adjective?

   My birthday present included two theater tickets.

   verb noun adjective

3. The following sentence contains either a simile or a metaphor. Which is it? What are the two things being compared?

   Nathan stood perfectly straight; he looked as rigid as an old oak tree that refuses to be moved by ravaging winds.

   simile metaphor ______________________

4. The prefix *anti-* means "against or opposite;" the prefix *ante-* means "before." Write each word next to its meaning.

   antebellum antiwar antecedent antiseptic

| | |
|---|---|
| A) | comes before something |
| B) | prevents infection |
| C) | before the war |
| D) | against war |

5. **Many words that end in *-f* or *-fe* form the plural by ending in *–ves*.**
   **Examples:** thief ➡ thieves knife ➡ knives Make these nouns plural.

   dwarf ➡ ______________ hoof ➡ ______________

6. **Use a colon only after an independent clause. Do not use it after a verb.** **Example:** Cities with the highest population are Chicago, Houston, Dallas, Detroit, and Austin. (No colon is needed because the predicate nominatives are linked to the subject by the verb *are*.) Is the colon used correctly in the following sentence?

To make brownies, you need: eggs, flour, sugar, and cocoa.

Yes No

7. **An independent clause or a sentence always expresses a complete thought.** Put a ✓ next to each independent clause.

| | | | |
|---|---|---|---|
| ____ | since it is raining | ____ | there is no outdoor recess |
| ____ | unless the sun comes out | ____ | we can still have fun |

8 – 12. Think about something that Benjamin Franklin said: "He that is good at making excuses is seldom good at anything else." Do you agree? Write your thoughts about this quote below.

______________________________________________

______________________________________________

______________________________________________

______________________________________________

______________________________________________

______________________________________________

______________________________________________

______________________________________________

# Lesson #100

1. **Consume or Devour?** Both of these words can mean "eat greedily" or "use up in an exaggerated way." The word *devour* usually has a more destructive connotation. Decide which word – *consume* or *devour* – has the most appropriate connotation for each sentence.

   The hungry wolf (consumed / devoured) the flesh of its prey.

   Most American children (consume / devour) too much sugar.

2. Underline two synonyms.

   urgent social critical trivial

3. Choose the word that completes this analogy.

   *Inferior* is to *ideal* as *tainted* is to ________.

   spoiled pure taunted pollution

4. The prefix *neo-* means "new." Another word for *beginner* is

   nephew neophyte noncompliant neural

5. Find these adjectives in a thesaurus or dictionary. Underline the adjective that best completes the sentence.

   The air was filled with the __________ smell of skunk.

   acrid incense expedient

6. **Many words that end in *-f* or *-fe* simply add *–s* to form the plural.**
   **Example:** giraffe ➡ giraffes Make these nouns plural.

   café ➡ ____________________ carafe ➡ ____________________

7. Choose the verbs that agree.

   Congress (begin / begins) its next session in about a week. The House of Representatives (has /have) been meeting continuously.

8. Write I if the clause is independent; write D if it is a dependent clause.

____While you are working on your collages, ____we will listen to music.

____You can talk quietly ____until the bell rings.

9. Underline the relative pronoun and dependent clause in this sentence.

Several trees that are diseased will need to be cut down.

10. Which sentence contains an action verb?

____ The Lipizzaner Stallions will march proudly all the way through the parade route.

____ They are huge and beautiful horses.

11. Cross out the fragment.

Would you do me a favor? I need you to get the notes I left next to the telephone. Or maybe on my desk. Just find them, please.

12. Rewrite the fragment above as a sentence that expresses a complete thought.

______________________________________________________________

______________________________________________________________

______________________________________________________________

______________________________________________________________

______________________________________________________________

______________________________________________________________

## Lesson #101

1. Are any of these plurals misspelled? Use a dictionary to check. Then cross out any misspelled words and write them correctly below.

   kangaroos zooes photos videos

   ______________________________________________

2. Underline two antonyms in this sentence.

   Michael is extremely timid around adults, yet he is boisterous when he's with his friends.

3. Choose the word that completes this analogy.

   *Sanitize* is to *disinfect* as *decorate* is to _____.

   embellish demolish cleanse furniture

4. Is the homograph a verb or a noun?

   No one objected to the suggestion that we break for lunch early.

   verb noun

5. Match these word parts with their meanings.

   *ante-* *anti-* *neo-*

   ____________ ____________ ____________
   against new before

6. Which set of plurals has no errors?

   A) wifes, halves, beliefs

   B) wives, halfs, beliefs

   C) wives, halves, beliefs

7. A simple sentence contains a ____________ and a ____________.

8. **A hyphen is used between the tens and the ones place, when writing out the numbers twenty-one through ninety-nine. Examples:** thirty-four, fifty-one, ninety-seven Insert hyphens where they are needed in the following sentence.

I wrote a check for forty three dollars and ninety seven cents, but the amount should have been thirty seven dollars and sixty two cents.

9. ***Whose* is the possessive form of *who*; *who's* is the contraction for "who is."** Choose the correct pronoun.

(Whose / Who's) parents are coming to Open House?

10. **Bad or Badly? *Bad* is an adjective; *badly* is an adverb**. Incorrect ➡ My hair looks badly. (Your hair can't see, so it doesn't "look.") Correct ➡ My hair looks bad today. Use the adjective *bad* in a sentence of your own.

______________________________________________

11. Use the adverb *badly* in a sentence of your own.

______________________________________________

12. **People speak in run-on sentences, but run-ons are grammatically incorrect and difficult to understand in writing.** Rewrite this run-on so that it is correct. Use conjunctions, and break it into smaller sentences.

Babe Ruth hit his first home run as a major league player on May 6, and I was born on May 6 and I'm going to be a great ball player too and maybe I'll break Babe Ruth's record for home runs.

______________________________________________

______________________________________________

______________________________________________

______________________________________________

______________________________________________

## Lesson #102

1. **A hyphen is used when writing fractions. Examples:** one-fifth, two-thirds
Insert hyphens where they are needed in this sentence.

One fourth of twenty four is six.

2. Both of the words *weird* and *exotic* can mean "strange," but one of these words has a more positive connotation. Decide which word – *weird* or *exotic* – has the most appropriate connotation for each sentence below.

weird ➡ (peculiar, creepy, odd, bizarre)

exotic ➡ (unusual, foreign, interesting, striking)

The new exhibit at our zoo features (weird / exotic) birds from all over the world. Some of them look a little (weird / exotic) with their oversized beaks and oddly shaped feet.

3. Three of these words are synonyms. Cross out the word that doesn't belong.

relief nuisance annoyance irritation

4. Choose the correct homophones.

(Its / It's) not (to / too) late to qualify for a discount on your summer fees.

5. Scientists agree that the age of dinosaurs antedates the emergence of humankind. According to what you know about Latin roots, the underlined word probably means what?

A) comes before
B) comes after
C) coincides with
D) is opposite

6. Is there an acronym in the following sentence? If so, underline it.

We have D.E.A.R. (Drop Everything And Read) every day after lunch.

7. Write the correct abbreviations for these words.

September ➡ ________ South Dakota ➡ ________ Street ➡ ________

8. Choose the correct pronoun. (Hint: which sounds right: I voted for him [whom] or I voted for he [who]?)

For (who / whom) did you vote?

9. **Most nouns that end in –*o* add –*s* to form the plural, but some add –*es*; always use a dictionary to check if you are not sure of the spelling.**
**Examples:** zero ➡ zeros tomato ➡ tomatoes
Write the plural of potato.

________________________________________

10. **A dash is used between words within a sentence. It is longer than a hyphen and is used to show emphasis. Example:** A dash should be used for a special effect — do not overuse it. Rewrite this sentence using a dash instead of a comma.

I promised I would be here, here I am!

________________________________________________________________

11. A compound sentence contains ____________________ ____________________ ____________________.

12. Combine these sentences to make a compound sentence.

Alex wrote to Grandma. Grandma sent Alex an airline ticket.

________________________________________________________________

________________________________________________________________

________________________________________________________________

## Lesson #103

1. Make these nouns plural.

   chimney ➡ ____________ lobby ➡ ____________

2. Underline an antonym for the word *lethargic*.

   sluggish energetic weary tired

3. Which pair of words completes this analogy? sun : son :: ______ : ______

   moon : stars fun : work mother : daughter liar : lyre

4. The following sentence contains either a simile or a metaphor. Which is it? What are the two things being compared?

   Hailstones came crashing down on the roof like handfuls of marbles flung by an angry child.

   simile metaphor ____________________

5. According to what you know about Greek roots, which of these is probably the meaning of the word *neoformation*?

   A) a change in circumstances
   B) something that comes after
   C) a new growth or form
   D) an antidote

6. Rewrite this opinion as a fact.

   Dealing with unreliable lockers, having multiple teachers, and navigating crowded hallways are the things that make middle school so frustrating.

   ____________________

   ____________________

7. Choose the correct pronoun.

   The jacket probably belongs to (whoever / whomever) sits in that seat.

8. **A hyphen is sometimes used to join a prefix with a base word. The hyphen helps to make the word more clear. Examples:** post-test, mid-July
Insert hyphens where they are needed in these sentences.

A) I missed number twenty seven on the pre test.

B) It was a question about anti war demonstrations in the 1960's.

9. A complex sentence is made up of two clauses, one ________________

and one ________________________________.

10. **Notice that every clause has a subject and a predicate (verb).** Write I if the clause is independent; write D if it is dependent. Underline the subject of the clause.

___Now that everyone is here, ____we can eat!

11. Fix this run-on by inserting a ⊙ to show where the first sentence should end.

During softball season all the girls practice right after school then we usually end up at one of our houses for a snack, and we watch a DVD or we listen to music for a while.

12. Write a sentence about what you like to do after school. Use at least two adjectives.

________________________________________

________________________________________

________________________________________

________________________________________

________________________________________

________________________________________

# Lesson #104

1. Look at the following pairs of words. The words in each pair are synonyms, but one has a positive connotation and the other has a negative connotation. Sort the words into two categories and write them in the chart below.

notorious, famous    devour, consume    weird, exotic

complex, problematic    outspoken, loud    smirk, smile

| Positive | Negative |
|---|---|
| | |
| | |
| | |
| | |
| | |
| | |

2. Underline two synonyms.    glee    wrath    disgust    anger

3. See if you can arrange these words, which are borrowed from the Portuguese language, in the chart below. Use a dictionary if you need help.

albino    dodo    marmalade    flamingo    molasses

| | |
|---|---|
| A) | citrus fruit jelly |
| B) | fool |
| C) | thick, sweet syrup |
| D) | white |
| E) | large pink bird |

4. Which two are synonyms? Use a dictionary to check.

novel    nominal    new    nuance

5. Study the chart. Then write each word next to its meaning below.

| tri- | three |
|---|---|
| bi- | two |
| -ped- | foot |

biped bipolar triad

a group of three ____________________

having two poles ____________________

a two-legged support ________________

6. Find the meaning and pronunciation of the word *rancor* in a dictionary.

Which of these rhymes with *rancor*? dancer banker encore

Which word means almost the same as *rancor*? bitter unusual cultivator

7. Make these nouns plural.

banjo ➡ ______________ rodeo ➡ ______________

8 – 12. If you could be in charge of running your school for a day, what are some changes that you would make? Write at least five sentences. Include at least one of each: simple sentence, compound sentence, and complex sentence.

_______________________________________________

_______________________________________________

_______________________________________________

_______________________________

_______________________________

_______________________________

_______________________________

## Lesson #105

1. Look at the underlined word; choose an antonym which will change the meaning of the sentence.

   The main character was <u>valiant</u> during most of the film.

   brave gallant cowardly courageous

2. *Benefit* is to *detriment* as *prosperous* is to ________.

   affluent flourishing poor devious

3. A mathematical expression with two terms is a _________.

   triglyceride binomial multinational monacle

4. This sentence states an opinion. Change it a little to make it a fact.

   Orville and Wilbur Wright were two of the greatest inventors of all time.

   ______________________________________________

5. **Hyphens are used in some compound words. Examples:** merry-go-round, mayor-elect, cross-reference Insert two more hyphens.

   My sister in law is a fair-minded person.

6. **When adding a prefix to a word, do not change the spelling of the word or the prefix. Examples:** un + natural ➡ unnatural un + pleasant ➡ unpleasant
   Write the word with its prefix.

   re- + evaluate ➡ ______________________

7. Choose the pronoun that agrees with the subject.

   My luggage has name tags attached to (it / them).

8. **You can use a dash within a sentence for clarity**. Look at this sentence: I meant Cleveland, Tennessee, not Cleveland, Ohio. (This sentence is confusing because of all the commas.) Here is another way to write it: I meant Cleveland, Tennessee - not Cleveland, Ohio. (Using the dash makes this sentence clearer.) Rewrite this sentence using a dash.

Use the cart only for boxes, crates, and books, never a TV!

______________________________________________

9. The direct object receives the action of the verb. Underline the direct object. (*What* did the President veto?)

The President vetoed the bill.

10. Underline the past perfect form of the verb *lie*.

When the electricity went out, I had just lain on the couch to watch TV.

11 – 12. **Proof It!** Use two different editing marks to correct errors in the following sentences.

In 1873 the treaty that gave the United states it's independence was finally signed.

It was called the Treaty of Paris, even though was an agreement between Great Britain and and the newly founded United States of America.

## Lesson #106

1. **Critique or Criticize?** The word *criticize* can mean "to find fault" or "to judge harshly." The word *critique* may mean "to review" or "to analyze." Decide which word has the most appropriate connotation for the sentence below.

   The assignment was to read a novel and (critique / criticize ) it.

2. Underline two synonyms. fictitious factual fabricated freestyle

3. Underline the word that correctly completes the sentence.

   The rescue workers used a (flair / flare) to mark off the dangerous area.

4. The following sentence contains either a simile or a metaphor. Which is it? What are the two things being compared?

   Tory was as cheerful as a bluebird in the springtime.

   simile metaphor ______________________________

5. Use what you know about roots to match these words and meanings.

   | | |
   |---|---|
   | travels on foot | triangular |
   | three sided | two lenses |
   | bifocal | peddler |

6. Rewrite this name correctly. mr paul waters, sr

   ______________________________________________

7. Is there an acronym in the following sentence? If so, underline it.

   A class called "Trouble-shooting, Repair, And Computers for Kids" (T.R.A.C.K.) is being offered at the recreation center.

8. **A hyphen is used to separate words on two lines. The hyphen can only be used between syllables. Example:** The organization of retired military <u>person-nel</u> gathered to plan a meeting with the governor. Insert hyphens where needed in the following sentences.

   The bride to be wore a very old-fashioned dress. The dress had beau tiful lacework, twenty one buttons, and a long train.

9. Decide whether the indefinite pronoun is singular or plural, and choose the other pronoun that agrees.

   <u>Most</u> of the newspaper is mangled, so you may not be able to read (it / them).

   singular plural

10. Underline the prepositional phrase. Write the object of the preposition on the line.

    Julian's best friend, Alexis, lives across the street. ______________

**Proof It!** The following sentences have been edited. Rewrite them correctly below.

11. The first successful all open-heart surgery was performed by doctors Lillehei and Lewis in 1952 ⊙

    ______________________________________________

    ______________________________________________

12. The patient ~~whom is~~ ^was a five-year-old girl, who had been born with a (whole)^sp in her heart.

    ______________________________

    ______________________________

    ______________________________

    ______________________________

# Lesson #107

1. Underline two antonyms in this sentence.

   Mr. Hanley was shrewd at running a restaurant, but he was ignorant of basic cooking techniques.

2. Choose the word that completes this analogy.

   *Calculator* is to *classroom* as ________ is to ________.

   microscope : laboratory   letter : postal carrier

   physician : stethoscope   shovel : gardener

3. Is the homograph a verb or a noun?

   An <u>object</u> in the road caused cars and trucks to swerve erratically.

   verb   noun

4. A country governed by three leaders is a ________.

   monarchy   democracy   triarchy   dictatorship

5. Irregular plural nouns do not follow any rules such as "add *–s* or *–es*." The spelling of irregular plurals must be memorized. Write the plural forms of these nouns.

   child ➡ ________________   foot ➡ ________________

6. Write a subject pronoun that could replace the underlined noun.

   <u>Roxanne</u> likes to decorate the doors with colorful pinwheels.

   ________________________

7. **You will always find brackets [ ] in pairs. Brackets are used in dictionary definitions or to insert words into writing that is already within parentheses.** Insert brackets around the dates in the following sentence.

(Benjamin Franklin 1706 - 1790 had begun his career as a printer. )

**You will not use brackets very often, but you should know about this word: [sic].** When you see the word *sic*, usually in brackets, it means that something has been copied word for word, even if it is misspelled or is grammatically incorrect. **Example:** He said, "Jordan ain't [sic] here." (The writer is aware of the mistake but is quoting someone accurately.)

8 – 12. Picture the inside of your locker. (If you don't have a locker, picture the inside of a closet or dresser in your bedroom.) Is it organized or kind of a mess? Write a sentence that describes your locker (or closet), using a **simile** or **metaphor**. Then write four supporting sentences.

______________________________

______________________________

______________________________

______________________________

______________________________

______________________________

______________________________

______________________________

______________________________

## Lesson #108

1. **Lean or Scrawny?** When used as an adjective, *lean* means "having mostly muscle" or "having very little fat." The word *scrawny* has a similar meaning but the connotation is "too lean" or "exceptionally thin." Decide which word has the most appropriate connotation for each sentence.

   A) I made a sandwich with slices of ____________ roast beef.

   B) That ______________ kitten looks like it could use a good meal.

2. Three of these words are synonyms. Cross out the word that doesn't belong.

   ordinary abnormal regular average

3. See if you can arrange these words, which are borrowed from the Italian language, in the chart below. Use a dictionary if you need help.

   opera piano pizza solo

| Word | From an Italian word meaning... |
|---|---|
| A) | "soft and loud" |
| B) | "alone" |
| C) | "work" |
| D) | "pie" |

4. These words all contain the Latin root that means what?

   impediment pedestrian quadruped

   ______________________

5. Read this quote. "I don't know nothin' [sic] about what happened." What does [sic] mean?

   ______________________________________

6. **The word *en masse* is from the Latin, meaning "in a mass."** A mass is a large group, crowd, or a big bunch of something. Which of the following groups would move *en masse*? Check all that apply.

____ fans reacting to a touchdown at a football game

____ kids taking turns at a drinking fountain

____ people rushing out of a building that is on fire

____ children playing jump rope on the playground

7. Underline the word that best completes the sentence.

Henry and (I / me) are designing a robotics experiment.

8. Add the proper punctuation to this interjection within a quote.

No way exclaimed Joan.

9 – 12. The inside of my locker is like a tossed salad that someone left in the refrigerator too long. Sheets of notebook paper, like crumpled lettuce leaves stick out of every corner. A stray gym shoe, a broken ruler, and last winter's stocking cap. So many things are piled up and mixed together that sometimes I can't even find my books. Lately, I stand back when I get to the last number on my locker combination – who knows what may fall out when I open the door!

A) Insert the editing mark that tells you to indent.

B) Underline two similes in the paragraph.

C) Draw a line through any sentence fragments.

D) Rewrite any sentence fragments so they are complete sentences.

______________________________________________

______________________________________________

______________________________________________

______________________________________________

## Lesson #109

1. Is the demonstrative in this sentence a pronoun or an adjective?

   Remember, I showed you <u>this</u> last week.

   pronoun adjective

2. Write the plural forms of these nouns.

   man ➡ ____________ mouse ➡ ____________

3. The prefix *hemi-* means "half." What is a hemicycle?

   A) the shape of a half circle
   B) a severe storm
   C) a type of bicycle
   D) a circular saw

4. Add commas where they are needed in the following letter.

   Dear Mr. Keating

   Please send four autographed copies of your book to my bookstore in Nashville Tennessee. One copy is for the local library another will be donated to our middle school and the third book will be on display at the bookstore. Of course I will keep the fourth copy for myself!

   Sincerely

   Jack Nelson

5. Read this sentence. What is the action verb? What is the direct object?

   The cunning lion pursued its prey.

   action verb ➡ ____________ direct object ➡ ____________

6. Choose the verb that agrees.

   When we (celebrate / celebrates) *Cinco de Mayo,* we honor Mexican culture.

7. Raleigh read Cooper Lang's article in Kid Sport Magazine. It was called "How to Shape Up for Soccer," and was on pages 4 and 5 of the September 2007, Volume 3 edition. Look in the *Help Pages* to see how Raleigh should cite (list) this article in his bibliography. Write the citation (listing) correctly below.

______________________________________________

8. Let's review the principal parts of verbs. Study the example; then complete the chart.

| Present | Past | Present Participle | Past Participle |
|---|---|---|---|
| learn | learned | is learning | had learned |
| follow | | | |
| slide | | | |

9 – 12. The paragraph below contains several errors which are mechanical or grammatical. Find a sentence with no mistakes and underline it. Then use five different editing marks to correct errors in the other sentences.

Your brain it is the control center of your body, and it works day and night, without resting, even when you be asleep. Your brain is in charge of makeing sure you keep breathing and that your heart keeps pumping. The amazing brain allows you to memorize facts, feel emotions, and digest your food. believe it or not, your brain can accomplish all of these things at the same time

The Human Brain

## Lesson #110

1. **Tricked or Cheated?** Both words mean "deceived." But one of the words has a more negative connotation than the other. Decide which word – *tricked* or *cheated* – has the most appropriate connotation for each sentence, and fill it in below.

   A) On April Fool's Day our teachers ____________________ us by mixing up the class schedule.

   B) We felt ____________________ because the rain ended our game before we had a chance to tie up the score.

2. List the four demonstrative.

   ____________ ____________ ____________ ____________

3. Which of these is an antonym for the word *peaceful*?

   violent tranquil serene calm

4. **Some nouns keep the same spelling whether they are singular or plural. Examples:** deer, moose, sheep If you are not sure of the spelling of a plural, use a dictionary to check. Write the plural form of each noun.

   calf ➡ ____________ trout ➡ ____________ goose ➡ ____________

5. **The suffix –*ology* means "the study of". Example:** *Musicology* is the study of music. What is *numerology*?

   ________________________________________

6. Choose the correct pronoun.

   You and (me / I) were only ten years old in fifth grade.

7. Underline the predicate nominative.

   My nephew is an Eagle Scout.

8. Arrange these words, borrowed from other languages, in the chart below. Use a dictionary if you need help.

curry yoga pajamas bangle shampoo

| | |
|---|---|
| from Hindi, meaning "colored glass bracelet" | A) |
| from Tamil, meaning "sauce" | B) |
| from Persian, meaning "leg garment" | C) |
| from Hindi, meaning "to knead, press, massage" | D) |
| from Sanskrit, meaning "union" | E) |

Read the following paragraph before completing the rest of the items in this lesson.

Have you ever heard of deforestation? Deforestation - cutting down too many trees too quickly - threatens the lives of people and animals in many parts of the world. People who live near forests depend on the trees for shade, firewood, and nourishment. Also, forests are home to many species of animals. When animals lose their homes through deforestation, they become endangered and even extinct. Soil is kept in its place by the roots of trees, so deforestation allows soil to erode, or wash away. Soil erosion pollutes precious water sources, which are essential to the survival of people and animals. Furthermore, when nutrient-rich soil is lost, farmers are unable to grow their crops. With decreased food production, people suffer from malnutrition and starvation.

Source: HTTP://WWW.BOTANY.UWC.AC.ZA/ENVFACTS/FACTS/DEFORESTATION.HTM

9. The information in the paragraph is

A) mostly factual. B) mostly someone's opinion. C) both fact and opinion.

10. Deforestation is the cause of which of the following?

A) a shortage of firewood
B) loss of animal habitat
C) soil erosion
D) all of these

11. List two effects of soil erosion, which are mentioned in the paragraph above.

______________________________

12. According to the paragraph, what is the definition of *deforestation*?

______________________________

**Lesson #111**

1. Choose the best demonstrative to complete this sentence.

   (That / Those) tomatoes are so ripe!

2. Choose the word or words that best complete this analogy.

   *Film* is to *theater* as ________________ is to *stadium.*

   popcorn football game goal line referee

3. Underline the homophone that correctly completes the sentence.

   Dustin is thought to be arrogant, since he is always putting on (airs / heirs).

4. What is the plural form of each noun? Use a dictionary if you need help.

   fish ➡ ________________ offspring ➡ ________________

   sheep ➡ ________________ headquarters ➡ ________________

5. The study of the <u>effect of time on living things</u> is ________________.

   biology chronobiology biophysics geology

6. Place commas where they are needed in the following sentence.

   Well I tried to call you and I rang your doorbell.

7. Insert the <u>future perfect form</u> of the verb *lie.*

   If you stay on the recliner until 5:00, you will have ________________ in the sun for four hours!

8. Match these subjects with their verbs.

| | |
|---|---|
| I | is |
| She | were |
| They | am |

Nobel Peace Prize winner, Wangari Maathai, realized that one of the only ways to fight deforestation is by planting indigenous trees. (Indigenous trees are the trees that grow naturally in a certain area.) In 1977, Professor Maathai began working with the women of Kenya to plant trees in her homeland. In addition to preserving the environment for future generations, planting trees helped the women to earn an income, so that they could feed and take care of their children. Led by Wangari Maathai, this tree-planting operation, which became known as the Green Belt Movement, planted tens of millions of trees. Wangari Maathai continues the struggle to preserve the environment by working with the United Nations, corporations, youth groups, and the Green Belt Movement International.

Source: HTTP://WOMENSHISTORY.ABOUT.COM/OD/WANGARIMAATHAI

9. Which of the following is not a synonym for the word *indigenous*?

native foreign home-grown local

10. Read the sentence. Because Wangari Maathai saw the need to repair the environment and create employment for women in Kenya, she organized the women and they began to plant trees. Does the underlined part state a cause or an effect?

cause effect

Read the next two sentences. Choose *simple*, *compound*, or *complex* to identify the type of sentence that it is.

11. Although the Green Belt Movement began in Kenya, it is now a worldwide effort.

simple compound complex

12. Everyone can do something to improve the environment, and it is each person's responsibility to do so.

simple compound complex

## Lesson #112

1. Look at the following pairs of words. The words are synonyms, but one has a positive connotation and the other has a negative connotation. Sort the words into two categories and write them in the chart below.

criticize, critique | lean, scrawny | cheat, trick

rigorous, demanding | abrupt, rude | snooping, curious

| Positive | Negative |
|---|---|
| | |
| | |
| | |
| | |
| | |
| | |

2. See if you can arrange these words, which are borrowed from the Italian language, in the chart below. Use a dictionary if you need help.

traffic confetti volcano stiletto graffiti

| | |
|---|---|
| A) | "small sweet thrown at carnivals" |
| B) | "scribbling" |
| C) | "small dagger" |
| D) | "to trade" |
| E) | the Roman god of fire |

3. Underline the homophone that correctly completes the sentence.

Mrs. Davenport has a large family and many (airs / heirs).

4. Underline two synonyms.

mobile ingenious movable stationary

5. Remember to use a colon before a list only if an independent clause comes first. Which is correct? Underline it.

Everyone else was on time: Rita, Phil, Noreen, and Joshua.

I brought: doughnuts, juice, napkins, and fruit.

6. What is the plural form of each noun? Use a dictionary if you need help.

species ➡ ____________ barracks ➡ ______________

perch ➡ ____________

7. The prefix *circum-* means "around." What is *circumference*?

_______________________________________________________________

8. Underline the adverb in this sentence. Which word does the adverb modify?

Nina played the cello brilliantly while we danced. ______________

9 – 12. Here is a quote from an interview with Wangari Maathai on November 12, 2004.

"I also have a lot of hope in youth. Their minds do not have to be held back by old thinking about the environment. And you don't have to be rich or give up everything to become active. Even simply using both sides of a piece of paper before recycling is conserving the environment."

Think about what Wangari Maathai is saying to young people about their role in preserving the environment. Write your thoughts about this quote below.

_______________________________________________________________

_______________________________________________________________

_______________________________________________________________

_______________________________________________________________

## Lesson #113

1. For each sentence, tell whether the underlined verb is transitive or intransitive.

   A) Every Sunday my Dad works the crossword puzzle in the newspaper. _____

   B) Then he works out at the YMCA for a few hours. _________

2. Complete the chart.

| Present | Past | Present Participle | Past Participle |
|---|---|---|---|
| believe | | is believing | |
| | tried | | has tried |
| | | is catching | |

3. **An adjective is any word that modifies a noun or a pronoun. Nouns are used as adjectives when they describe other nouns. Examples:** *tennis* racket, *lake* house, *Columbus* schools Underline all the nouns used as adjectives.

   Where is my party dress? I saw it in the coat closet. Okay, where is my winter shawl? Look in your dresser drawers.

4. Insert hyphens where they are needed. (Use the *Help Pages* if you do not remember how.)

   In physical education class we did push ups, sit ups, and twenty one laps around the gym.

5. Add commas to punctuate this sentence correctly.

   We will grill the hamburgers not the hotdogs for lunch.

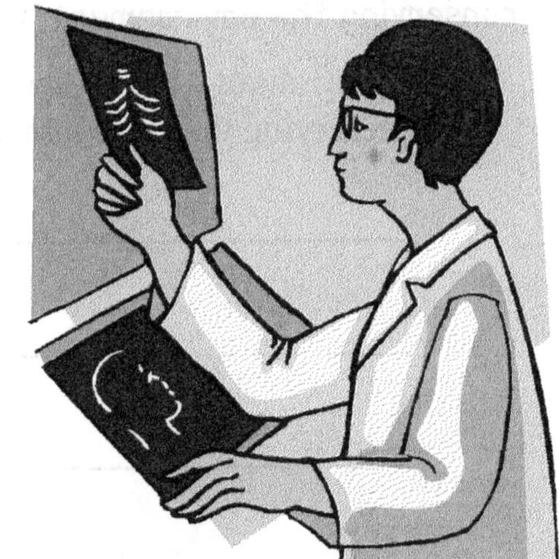

6. Remember, *-ology* refers to the study of something. See if you can complete the chart by filling in the name of each branch of knowledge. Choose from the list.

biology psychology radiology mythology astrology

| | |
|---|---|
| A) | the study of human behavior |
| B) | myths, stories, beliefs |
| C) | how heavenly bodies affect humans |
| D) | the science of living things |
| E) | the science of x-rays and nuclear radiation |

7. Underline the collective noun; choose the verb that agrees.

Each family (bring / brings) a salad, dessert, or appetizer to the picnic.

8. Alice used the book, Cowboys of the Wild West, by Russell Freedman for her research paper. The book was published in New York by Scholastic Incorporated in 1985. Look in the *Help Pages* to see how Alice should cite this article in her bibliography. Write the citation correctly below.

______________________________________________

9. Complete the sentence with a form of the verb *be* that agrees with the subject.

Mother's Day ________ first celebrated in 1914 during the month of May.

10. Write these words with their suffixes.

submit + -ed ➡ ______________ program + -ing ➡ ______________

11. **When writing a title, capitalize the first and last word and all other important words.** Do not capitalize articles (a, an, the), conjunctions, or prepositions that have less than five letters. Write this book title correctly.

the day the clowns came to perry ➡ ______________________

12. Where would you look to find out if a book has a chapter about friendship?

A) index B) appendix C) table of contents D) glossary

## Lesson #114

1. **Plan, Plot, or Scheme?** All three words have to do with coming up with an idea. But the word *plot* means "to plan secretly" or "plan illegally." A *scheme* may be a plan that is a little outrageous. Decide which word – *plan, plot,* or *scheme* – has the most appropriate connotation for each sentence, and fill it in below.

   A) The security guards were able to disrupt the terrorists' ____________________ to kidnap a government official.

   B) My goal is to maintain a grade point average of 3.5 or better, but I need to develop a study ____________________ that will fit my schedule.

   C) The backyard carnivals and citywide garage sales were part of a ________________ to raise money for our new playground.

2. Add punctuation. Insert a comma, a hyphen, quotation marks, and an end mark into the following sentence.

   Instead of writing an essay I want you to read chapter thirty three: What's Between the Lines

3. Fill in a conjunction to complete the sentence.

   Neither the squad master, ______________ his assistant had the clipboard.

4. Write the plural forms of these nouns.

   goose ➡ ____________________ louse ➡ ________________________

5. Complete the sentence by adding the future perfect form of the verb *begin*.

   I'm sure the performance __________ __________ ___________ by now.

6. Write C next to each clause and P next to each phrase.

____ will be planting ____ you understand

____ were dancing and singing

7. Is the verb in the following sentence transitive?

We stocked the shelves with plenty of supplies.

____ No, it is not transitive.

____ Yes, and the direct object is ____________________.

8. Underline the acronyms. OSHA DARE YWCA PTO

9. Add a semicolon.

Officer Paulette was our DARE instructor now she teaches at the Police Academy.

10 – 12. Study the prefix chart. Then use the word list to complete the sentences below.

anthropology bibliotherapy centripetal

| *centri -* | center |
|---|---|
| *biblio-* | book |
| *anthropo-* | man |

A) The counselor uses picture books during the children's __________________________ session.

B) The ______________________________ force causes movement toward the center.

C) _________________________ is the study of humans and their society.

## Lesson #115

1. Choose the word that completes this analogy.

   *Swear* is to *sworn as weave* is to ________________.

   woven knit torn worn

2. Is the homograph a verb or a noun?

   His wound required medical attention and resulted in several stitches.

   verb noun

3. Insert a semicolon where it is needed.

   Katrina plays the violin and Jackie is studying cello they can play duets.

4. Check the spelling of the words in this sentence. Use the editing mark for "check spelling" to mark any words that may be misspelled.

   Mrs. Smith was very appreciateive of your help.

5. Add a comma after the prepositional phrase.

   Instead of going to the park we can shoot baskets in the driveway.

6. Underline the object of the preposition.

   I'd like to ride with you.

7. **Some nouns name things that only come in pairs: scissors, pajamas, trousers. These nouns always take a plural verb. Example:** the scissors are
   Choose the verb that agrees.

   (Is / Are) my jeans in the dryer?

8. Match these subjects with their verbs.

| | |
|---|---|
| Neither | were |
| Several | was |

9. Choose the correct words from the following list to complete the sentences below.

sources credit plagiarism stealing illegal consequences

Copying someone else's work is called ________________. This is a serious form of cheating with serious ______________. Plagiarism is both illegal and against school rules because plagiarism is a form of __________.

10 – 12. Read the following set of directions and use it to create a flow chart below. The flow chart should show at least five steps that must be completed.

First, work with a partner to brainstorm a list of film titles; try to list at least fifty. Then join with another pair of students, and compare your lists. Cross out titles that were repeated, and write down any new titles that you think of. Make sure you have exactly one hundred titles all together. Then, sort the films according to the number of words in each title. Put them in three categories: one-word, two-words, and three-or-more-words. Finally, create a circle graph which shows the percentages of one-word, two-word, and three-plus-word titles.

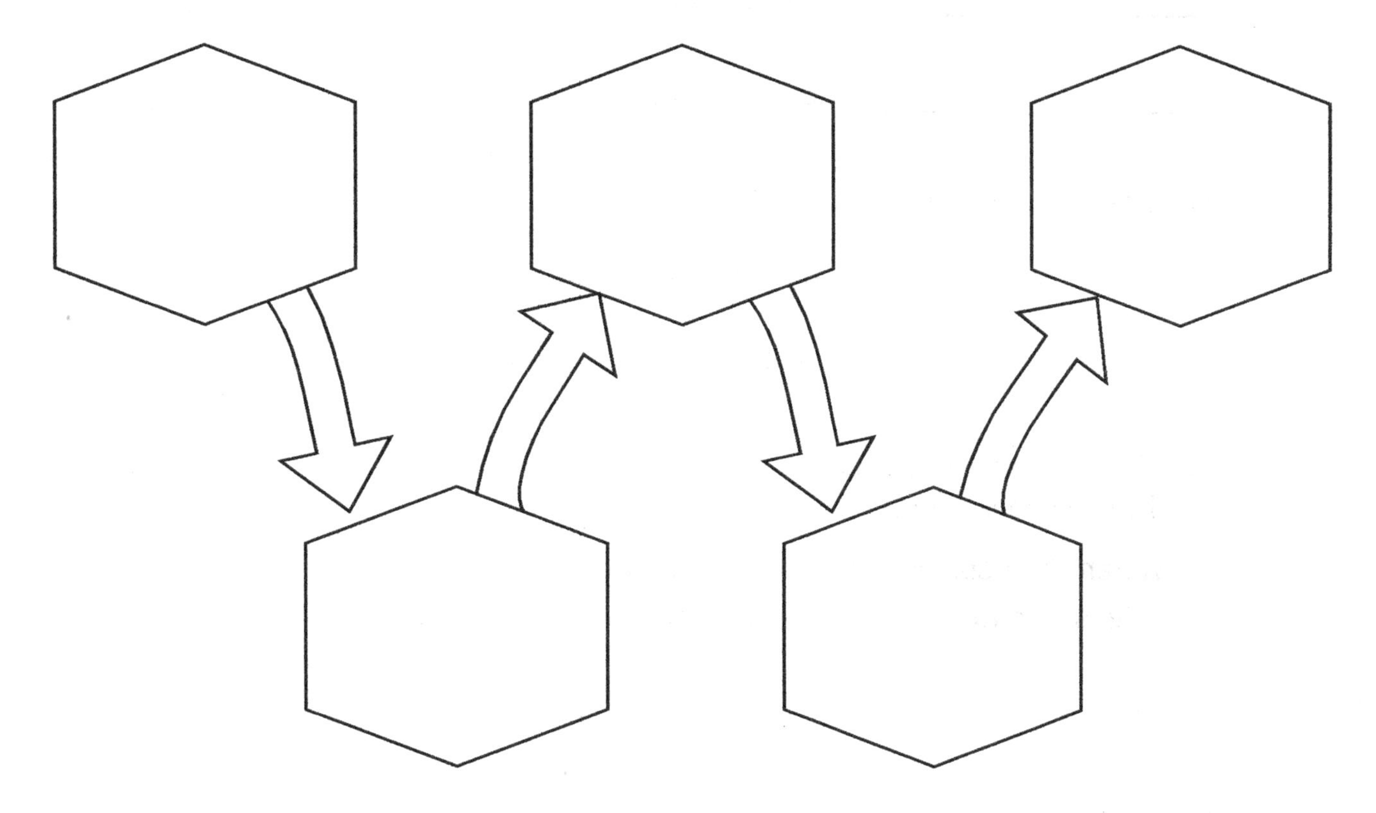

# Lesson #116

1. **Assertive or Pushy?** Both words can mean "forceful." But the word *assertive* has a connotation of "confidence," whereas *pushy* implies "annoying." Decide which word – *pushy* or *assertive* – has the most appropriate connotation for each sentence, and fill it in below.

   A) Don't be so ____________________; you know it is impolite to go out of turn.

   B) It is important to speak your mind, so be ____________________ when you have an opportunity to talk.

2. Underline the indefinite pronoun, and choose the verb that agrees.

   Neither of the twins (like / likes) chocolate milk.

3. There are many words borrowed from other languages, which name a spacious porch on a large house: veranda, piazza, loggia, lanai, terrace, and patio. Choose three of these words and look them up in a dictionary. Then list the words and their language of origin below.

   ____________________ comes from ____________________.

   ____________________ comes from ____________________.

   ____________________ comes from ____________________.

4. Is the homograph a verb or a noun?

   We <u>wound</u> the garden hose neatly and stored it in the garage.

   verb noun

5. The following sentence contains either a simile or a metaphor. Which is it? What are the two things being compared?

   When it's nearing his bedtime, my baby brother is a tempest, unleashing his stormy wrath throughout our house.

   simile metaphor ____________________

6. Check the spelling of the words in the sentence below. If a word is misspelled, cross it out and write it correctly on the line.

The whether is very changeable today.

______________________________

7. Add the proper punctuation to this interjection within a quote.

Way to go Now we qualify for the state finals.

8. Choose the correct verb.

The orchestra always (enter / enters) the stage from the left.

9. **If you want to use the plural form of a noun such as pants, binoculars, or scissors, use the word *pairs*. Examples:** two pairs of scissors, nine pairs of pants Choose the verb that agrees.

There (are / is) several pairs of tweezers in the clinic.

10. Which part of speech should rarely be used in formal writing?

| adverb | adjective | conjunction | interjection |
|---|---|---|---|
| noun | preposition | pronoun | verb |

11 – 12. Think about things that make you smile: scenes from a comedy show, touching the soft fur of a kitten, memories of something funny, the smell of barbeque, hearing a joke, or a really tasty treat. Make a list of things that make you smile; try to use the memory of all of your senses.

______________________________

______________________________

______________________________

______________________________

______________________________

## Lesson #117

1. Three of these words are synonyms. Cross out the word that doesn't belong.

   cautious vigilant inattentive watchful

2. **When writing a title, capitalize the first and last word and all other important words.** Do not capitalize articles (a, an, the), conjunctions, or prepositions that have less than five letters. Write this book title correctly.

   misadventures at camp Ketchikan ______________________

3. Complete the chart.

| Present | Past | Present Participle | Past Participle |
|---|---|---|---|
| notice | noticed | is noticing | have noticed |
| speak | | | |

4. Check the spelling of the words in this sentence. Mark any misspelled words.

   The operator was beseiged with calls from local resadents.

5. According to what you know about roots and prefixes, the word *anthropocentric* probably means ______________.

   A) a four-legged creature
   B) centered on humankind
   C) government by the people
   D) the distance around something

6. Add the necessary comma to this sentence.

   On the other hand the weather may be mild.

7. What is the direct object in this sentence?

   Congress passed the bill.

   A) congress
   B) passed
   C) bill
   D) There is no object in this sentence.

8. **Remember, a clause has a subject and a verb.** Write C next to each clause and P next to each phrase.

____ at my school ____ while we were eating

____ before classes started

9. Put a ✓ next to the sentence that states an opinion.

____ Completing a Sudoku puzzle is fun, but it is also challenging and takes plenty of patience.

____ Researchers say that most people spend between 10 and 30 minutes solving a Sudoku puzzle, depending on their level of skill and experience.

10. What part of a science book would give you the definition of photosynthesis?

A) index B) glossary C) title page D) table of contents

11. Look at the underlined word; choose an antonym which will change the meaning of the sentence.

Everyone in our league has begun to <u>despise</u> the teams from the North side.

admire detest scorn loathe

12. Add punctuation. Insert an apostrophe, quotation marks, a comma, and hyphens into this sentence.

Catherine s name means pure and she is my new sister in law.

## Lesson #118

1. Write the plural form of each noun. Use a dictionary to check your work.

   fez ➡ __________ hobby ➡ ______________ tiptoe ➡ __________

2. The words *wild* and *energetic* both refer to an active state. But one of the words has a more positive connotation than the other. Decide which word – *wild* or *energetic* – has the most appropriate connotation for each sentence, and fill it in below.

   wild ➡ frantic, uncivilized, unrestrained

   energetic ➡ lively, active, brisk

   A) The audience howled like ________________ animals until the band returned to the stage.

   B) The ____________________ performers were able to sing and dance for hours.

3. Choose the correct verb.

   I, unlike my sister, (am / is / are) going to take an art class this summer.

4. Choose the word that completes this analogy.

   *Zoologist* is to *animals* as *psychologist* is to ___.

   planets diseases psychology people

5. Check the spelling of these words. If a word is misspelled, cross it out and write it correctly on the line.

   hankercheif leisure amusement

   ________________________________________

6. The Greek root *-morph-* refers to "form." Which word means "to give something human form?"

   morphine anthropomorphic anthropology morphology

7. Complete the sentence with a form of the verb *be* that agrees with the subject.

Nothing ____________ impossible today!

8. Underline the relative pronoun and dependent clause in this sentence.

I earned every cent that was spent on my bicycle, by mowing lawns.

9. Underline the simple predicate.

Henry walked two dogs all around the neighborhood.

10 – 12. Take a look at Nick's paragraph, which is written below. Nick has a great idea for a holiday, but his writing has a few errors. Use the checklist below to make corrections.

If I could design a national holiday it would Oreo Day! First, people would go out and buy a bag of Oreos. After a while, chefs of all ages would create the wildest and tastiest Oreo creations, like fried Oreos. Or something like that. Also there would be games like "Oreo Toss," where the players would try and toss as many Oreos as possible into a bucket of milk. Guys who are in love would give girls Oreos on this day Oreo Day would be sweet people would love it.

____ Is the paragraph indented? If not, insert the editing mark for "indent."

____ Are there any fragments? If so, draw a line through the fragments.

____ Are there any run-ons? If so, use editing marks to fix any run-ons, or rewrite the sentences correctly below.

______________________________________________

______________________________________________

______________________________________________

# Lesson #119

1. **Homonym Riddle:** This word names "a place where someone is buried" or "a cause for great alarm." What is it?

   ______________________

2. Are these words spelled correctly? Cross out any misspellings.

   emabrassment    patroller    carrying

3. An organism which is *monomorphic* probably has ________.

   A) something to do with books    C) a single form

   B) the ability to live on land and in water    D) two feet

4. Place commas where they are needed in the following sentence.

   "Is there already an office in Beirut" asked Lisa "or will they be building one soon?"

5. Complete the sentence by adding the present perfect form of the verb *run*.

   Ronnie ____________ ____________ track all through high school.

6. Choose verbs that agree with the indefinite pronoun subjects of these sentences.

   Little (is / are) expected; anything (is / are) possible, however.

7. Write the correct abbreviations for these words.

   November ➡ ________ New York ➡ ________ Mister ➡ ________

8. Underline the complete subject.

   Some of the best children's books were written by Judy Blume.

9. Choose the correct words from the following list to complete the sentences below.

sources credit plagiarism cite illegal consequences

In order to avoid plagiarism you should never turn in something that you copied from someone else. You may be able to download and print information off the internet. But it is A)__________ to put your name on it and hand it in for B)__________. You will find information in books, magazines, or encyclopedias that you can use for your report. But you must write the information your own words. Also, you need to C)__________ your D)__________ by listing the names of the authors whose work you used.

10 – 12. Proofread Grace's paragraph, and complete the checklist below.

I think that a lot of ways that people get paid are so unfair. Entertainers and sports players have fun doing what they do and get paid millions of dollars. While police officers and firefighters are out there risking their lives every day, and they don't get paid nearly as much. Same with teachers. No one would be anywhere without teachers.

____ Underline Grace's topic sentence.

____ Find a fragment, and draw a line through it. Rewrite the fragment as a complete sentence.

________________________________________

________________________________________

________________________________________

________________________________________

____ One of the sentences is a dependent clause. Use an editing mark to show that the coordinate conjunction should be removed. Then, add the editing mark for capitalization to the word that should begin the sentence.

# Lesson #120

1. **Petite or Puny?** Both words mean "small." But the word *petite* has a much less harsh connotation than *puny*. The word *puny* connotes "ill-health." Decide which word – *petite* or *puny* – has the most appropriate connotation for each sentence, and fill it in below.

   A) The ______________________ and graceful ballerina seemed to float like a fairy princess across the stage.

   B) All of the puppies were sold, except for the little one; he is so ______________________ that people think he might be sick.

2. The four words below can have similar meanings. They all describe porches or walkways. Find each of these words in a dictionary and write the language of origin next to each word.

| Word | Language of Origin |
|---|---|
| portico | A) |
| colonnade | B) |
| gallery | C) |
| balcony | D) |

3. Look at the underlined homonyms. Write a V above the verb and an A above the adjective.

   We will <u>exact</u> payment on the first day of each month.

   I will let you know the <u>exact</u> amount that is due.

4. The following sentence contains either a simile or a metaphor. Which is it? What are the two things being compared?

   That little dog is so attached to you; he's a fuzz ball on Velcro.

   simile      metaphor      ______________________________

5. A bibliography is a list of ______________.

   A) sciences   B) topics   C) sources   D) stories

6. Check the spelling of the words in this sentence. Use the editing mark for "check spelling" to mark any words that may be misspelled.

Give the anceint key to it's owner.

7. Choose the correct word to modify the verb.

Your writing is neat, but you write so (slow / slowly)!

8. Underline the prepositional phrase in this sentence. What is the object of the preposition?

Various paintings were on display throughout the museum. __________

9. Complete the sentence by adding the present perfect form of the verb *choose*.

My family ______ _______________ to celebrate the holidays at home.

10 – 12. Kristen's description of a dessert that she would invent sounds yummy. But her writing has a few mistakes. Read the paragraph and complete the checklist.

If I could invent a special desert it would be called Candy Cake. Candy Cake is made of all diferent kinds of hard candy: suckers Jolly Ranchers gumdrops and mints. You grind the candy up, and put it in the oven till it is all melted. While you are waiting, start to make the dough for the cake. You need eggs, water and cake mix. Bake the cake in the oven when the melted candy is done you spread it on top of the cake like frosting.

____ Mark two spelling errors.

____ Correct a run-on, by adding the editing marks for end punctuation and capitalization.

____ Add commas to a series.

## Lesson #121

1. Underline all the nouns used as adjectives.

   Marcie eats Brazil nuts and sunflower seeds at snack time and she likes carrot cake or rice pudding for dessert.

2. Fill in *verbs of being* that agree with the subjects of these sentences.

   Last summer Alexandra __________ not able to visit the Eiffel Tower.

   However, we ____________ going to schedule another tour soon.

3. Choose the correct word to modify the verb.

   Coach Jacobs has always treated us (fair / fairly), and we respect him.

4. Change the meaning of the sentence below by underlining an antonym for *purify*. Use a dictionary if you need help.

   We will learn about some additives that may purify a solution.

   A) combine B) contaminate C) scorch D) disinfect

5. According to what you know about roots and suffixes, the word *morphology* probably means what?

   A) the study of the form of things
   B) a branch of knowledge
   C) changing form
   D) the study of living things
   E) a computer technique

6. Check the spelling of the words in the following sentence; cross out the misspelled word and write it correctly on the line.

   That blue piece isn't even noticable. ____________________________

7. Which of these is a subordinate clause?

   ____ now that we have finished sixth grade

   ____ we can choose a foreign language to study

Read the following paragraph before completing the next two items.

When deciduous trees change color during the fall, it is because there is not enough light to keep photosynthesis going in the leaves. The chlorophyll that plants use during photosynthesis is green, so when photosynthesis stops, the green color fades away. The leaves revert back to other colors that were hidden under the green. The leaves are most vibrant and magnificent just before they die and fall off the trees.

8. Underline a sentence in the paragraph that states an opinion.

9. A clause from the first sentence is re-written below. Does this clause state a fact or an opinion?

...there is not enough light to keep photosynthesis going in the leaves.

fact opinion

10 – 12. **Proof it.** Use editing marks to correct Shannon's writing sample.

The most difficult thing about being a girl my age is that you get more responsibilitys. Also Peer pressure. Because you think you wanna listen to your friends so they wont get mad at you. but you really don't want to listen to them.

## Lesson #122

1. Look at the following pairs of words. The words are synonyms but one has a positive connotation and the other has a negative connotation. Sort the words into two categories and write them in the chart below.

pushy, assertive    energetic, wild    scheme, plot
admire, envy    petite, puny    sneer, grin

| Positive | Negative |
|---|---|
| | |
| | |
| | |
| | |
| | |
| | |

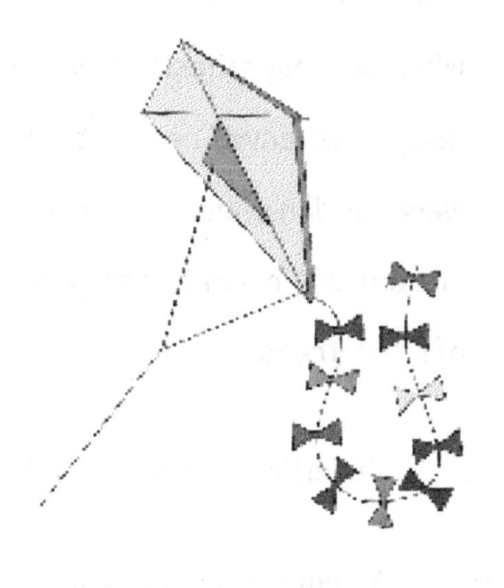

2. Which pair of correlative conjunctions will best complete the sentence?

Ms. Norman tries to give you a lot of opportunities to succeed. In her class, you get daily points ______________ for your class work, ______________ for your cooperation and behavior.

either/or    not only/but also    whether/or    neither/nor

3. Underline the correct homophone; use a dictionary if you need help.

The kite runner loosened his grip on the (real / reel), and the kite soared away.

4. A member of a political party of the Center may be called a(n) _______.

A) Democrat    B) Republican    C) Independent    D) Centrist

5. Add commas to punctuate this sentence correctly.

   On July 17 1998 we drove through Ohio Kentucky and Tennessee.

6. How have you been acting lately? Is your behavior *narcissistic* or *altruistic*—or a little of both? Choose the word that you think fits you best, and then find its meaning in a dictionary or thesaurus. Write the meaning of the word you chose here.

   ___________________________________________

7. Underline two synonyms. spacious divider partition placement

8. Choose the correct words from the following list to complete the sentences below.

   sources bibliography credit plagiarism encyclopedias

   There are ways to avoid A)________________. One way is to cite all your B)______________, by listing them in a C)________________. Never copy another writer's work; take careful notes, and put the information in your own words. If you do quote someone, be sure to use quotation marks around the author's exact words and give D)______________ by including the name of the speaker or writer.

9. Have you seen this symbol? What does it stand for?

   ___________________________________________

10. Complete the sentence by adding the past perfect form of the verb *cut*.

    Wilma __________ ____________ the fabric before she measured the table.

11. What does a declarative sentence do?

    tells something asks something gives a command shows strong feeling

12. Complete the chart.

| Present | Past | Present Participle | Past Participle |
|---|---|---|---|
| go | | | |
| skip | | | |

## Lesson #123

1. Are any of these plurals misspelled? Use a dictionary to check. Then rewrite any misspelled words correctly.

   tattoos memo's hooves

   ______________________________

2. Which of these words are prepositions?

   powerful always have lightly with among

3. Fill in verbs (*is* or *are*) that agree with the collective nouns in these sentences.

   The staff __________ meeting in the conference room. Each working group ____________ required to present its findings to the staff.

4. Underline an antonym for the word *corrupt*.

   shady fraudulent honest crooked

5. Choose the word pair that completes the analogy. banana : fruit :: _____ : _____

   felt : fabric singer : song rough : jagged pilot : jet

6. The prefixes *co-*, *com-*, and *con-* mean "together with." Match each word with its meaning.

   _____cooperate _____communicate _____conspire

   A) exchange information with
   B) get along with
   C) to secretly plan with others

7. Are these words spelled correctly? Cross out any misspellings.

   merriment slightly controler

8. An acronym is a word made from the beginning letters of other words. Which of the following is an acronym?

PTA RITA CYO USA

Where can you find the meaning of an acronym? ______________

9 – 12. Think about something Charles Shultz said: "Like a ten-speed bike, most of us have gears we do not use." Write about what this quote means to you. Write at least five sentences.

_______________________________________________

_______________________________________________

_______________________________________________

_______________________________________________

_______________________________________________

_______________________________________________

_______________________________________________

_______________________________________________

_______________________________________________

## Lesson #124

1. Look at the following pairs of words. Their meanings may be similar, but one of the two has a positive connotation and the other has a negative connotation. Sort the words into two categories and write them in the chart below.

trickster, villain distinctive, peculiar nosy, curious

weird, exotic complex, problematic

| Positive | Negative |
|---|---|
| | |
| | |
| | |
| | |
| | |

2. See if you can arrange these words, which are borrowed from African or Arabic languages, in the chart below. Use a dictionary if you need help.

banana cola safari coffee zebra

| | |
|---|---|
| A) | soft drink made from kola nuts |
| B) | African mammal |
| C) | yellow tropical fruit |
| D) | beans that grow in tropical climates |
| E) | a journey or expedition |

3. Underline each interjection. Hey, what's up? Oh boy, have I got news for you!

4. What part of a book lists all the page numbers on which a word is mentioned?

A) index B) glossary C) appendix D ) table of contents

5. Is the homograph a verb or a noun? verb noun

It is a crime for military personnel to <u>desert</u> an assigned station.

6. Here are more words with the prefixes that mean "together with." Write each word next to its meaning. Use a dictionary if you need help.

coexist cohesion compress compromise consolidation

| | |
|---|---|
| A) | to press together |
| B) | an agreement or settlement |
| C) | to exist (live) together |
| D) | sticking or working together |
| E) | bringing things together |

7. Add commas where they are needed.

Anthony please bring the paints water and brushes.

8. Write the meaning of the abbreviation. Inc. ➡ ______________________

9. Carlos read the book, Looking at Weather by David Suzuki. The book was published in New Work by John Wiley & Sons, Inc. in 1991. Write the entry that Carlos will use for his bibliography below. (Use the *Help Pages* if you do not remember how.)

_______________________________________________

10. Complete the sentence by adding the future perfect form of the verb *dig*.

By the end of the summer, those groundhogs __________ __________ __________ tunnels all through the yard.

11 – 12. Evaluate the following sentences; there is a grammatical error in each one. Circle each of the errors.

Each of the students carried their lunches in a backpack. The contents of the backpack also included: rain gear, a water bottle, and clean socks.

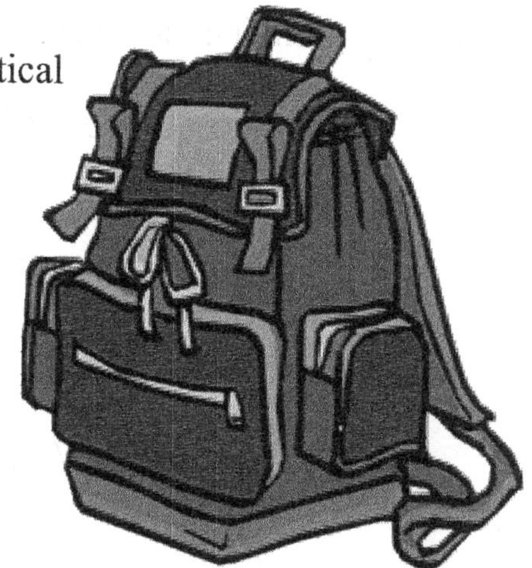

## Lesson #125

1. Rewrite the phrases, using the possessive form of the noun.
   **Example:** the flag of the country ➡ the country's flag

   the director of the film ➡ ______________________________

   the seeds of the tomato ➡ ______________________________

2. Complete the sentence with a form of the verb *be* that agrees with the subject.

   Each of the flowers _______ blooming brighter than the one before it!

3. Choose an antonym which will change the meaning of the sentence.

   My father loathes the taste of sauerkraut because he ate it frequently during the war.

   despises    enjoys    detests    abhors

4. The prefix *de-* usually means "the opposite" or "reverse" of something.
   **Examples:** decode, demobilize, deconstruct
   Choose one of the examples and write its definition here.

   ______________________________

5. Check the spelling of the words in this sentence. Use the editing mark for "check spelling" to mark any words that may be misspelled.

   A foriegn government bought the equipment.

6. Combine these sentences and write a sentence with a compound predicate.

   Lucinda makes pottery. Lucinda sells her art at local fairs.

   ______________________________

7. Choose the correct pronoun.

   (Whoever / Whomever) wants to go should get into the car now.

8. Evaluate this statement; is it a fact, opinion, or a little of both? Explain below.

President Lyndon B. Johnson, one of the greatest presidents of all time, declared a "War on Poverty" in 1964.

______________________________________________

______________________________________________

9 – 12. **Proof it!** Below is what Frances wrote about fictional characters that she admires or despises. Use editing marks and the checklist below to mark any errors in her writing sample.

Many of my favorite and most despised fictional characters are from disney stories. Bell is one of my favorite disney characters because she always wears a beautiful dress, and her hair is always sensational. I also like Tinkerbelle. Her fairy form was very cute! One of the disney characters I despise is Ursula She is cruel and very treacherous. Cinderella's step-mother and step-sisters are also evil and vindictive.

____ Is there a topic sentence? If so, underline it. If not, write one below.

______________________________________________

____ Are all of the proper nouns capitalized? If not, mark them with the editing mark for capitalization.

____ Does each sentence begin with a capital letter and end with the proper punctuation? If not, use the editing marks to correct any errors.

____ Is the verb tense consistent throughout the paragraph? If not, cross out incorrect verbs, and insert correct ones.

## Lesson #126

1. Look at the following pairs of words. The words are synonyms but one has a positive connotation and the other has a negative connotation. Sort the words into two categories and write them below.

   flung, dropped    challenging, difficult    laughed, snickered

   nosy, interested    stubborn, willful    strict, severe

   Positive ➡ ______________________________

   Negative ➡ ______________________________

2. Choose the verb that agrees with the indefinite pronoun.

   Most of the tuna casserole (is / are) gone.

3. Choose the verb that agrees.

   Losing the game, after so many other disappointments, (was / were) just too much to bear.

4. Look at the underlined homonyms. Write a V above the verb and an N above the noun.

   Time flies when you're having fun, and fruit flies hang around overripe peaches.

5. Choose the pair that completes the analogy. *Mile* is to *feet* as ____________.

   liquid is to solid    liters is to gallon    inches is to area    kilometer is to meters

6. Underline the transitive verb and the direct object.

   Everyone who ate the chicken began to feel sick a few hours later.

7. Add commas if necessary.

   On the other side of the mountain the air was fresh and clear.

Study the prefix chart. Then use the words in the chart to complete the sentences below.

| Prefix | Meaning | Example Word |
|---|---|---|
| micro - | small | microbus |
| photo- | light | photometry |
| hydro- | water | hydrosphere |

8. ______________________________ is a type of physics that deals with the measurement of light.

9. We only have ten people, so we can all ride the ____________________.

10. All of the water in the atmosphere and on the surface of the earth

belongs to the ______________________________.

11 – 12. Below is Anna's account of how her friends would describe her. Her writing has a few errors, however. Read and revise Anna's paragraph. Find at least three grammatical or mechanical errors, and correct them with editing marks or notes in the margin.

My friends would describe me as nice, loyal, and sweet. Also funny, outgoing, friendly, and fun to be with. I can also sometimes be really goofy, crazy, and a big drama queen. I'm also helpful and considerate. when I want to do something I go all the way with it! I'm energetic, I get good grades, and I love sports and acting! And that's how my friends would of described me as.

## Lesson #127

1. Complete the sentence by adding the past perfect form of the verb *draw*.

   Mr. Oster __________ __________________ some sketches for the new building even before he met with the planning committee.

2. Choose a synonym which could replace the underlined word without changing the meaning of the sentence.

   Alaska is immense, with an area of over 1.5 million square kilometers.

   vast   frigid   isolated   rough

3. A microorganism is always very ________.

   A) tiny   B) dangerous   C) unusual   D) simple

4. Choose the missing letters.   ei   ie

   A synonym for snobbish is conc____ted.

5. Use this information to write a complex sentence.

   wants a cell phone, doesn't have a job

   ______________________________________________________

   ______________________________________________________

6. Write the correct abbreviations for these words.

   gallon ➜ _________   teaspoon ➜ ______   pint ➜ ___________

7. Complete the sentence by adding the present perfect form of the verb *fly*.

   My baby sister __________ _________________ in a jet many times.

8. Underline the antecedent of the relative pronoun in this sentence.

The kids whose houses are on Lake Avenue are picked up last.

9. Choose the pronoun that agrees with the subject (collective noun).

The symphony needs to raise enough money to cover (their / its) daily expenses.

10. Is this sentence simple, compound, or complex?

Troy will work with Dad until the painting is finished.

simple compound complex

**Proof It!** Take a look at the sentences below, which were written by John.

I would be willing to speek out against some one that has done something wrong. I wood hate to lose a frendship over something that i felt was wrong, but i need to stick to what i beleeve is right.

11. Use the editing mark for "check spelling" to correct four errors.

12. Use the mark for capitalization to correct three other errors.

# Lesson #128

1. **Outspoken or Blunt?** A person who "speaks her mind" may be called *outspoken* or *blunt*, but these words have different connotations. An *outspoken* person is direct, communicative, honest, open, and forthright. A person who is *blunt* is also direct, but in a way that may be harsh, frank, or abrupt. In which sentence below is the speaker *blunt*?

   ____ You are a couch potato; you need to get up and start exercising.

   ____ I believe you will feel healthier and look better if you get daily exercise.

Many common abbreviations are originally from Latin phrases. Study the chart below; then complete each of the following sentences with one of the abbreviations.

| Term | Abbreviation | Meaning |
|---|---|---|
| et alia | et. al. | "and others" |
| id est | i.e. | "that is to say" |
| anno Domini | A.D. | "in the year of the Lord" |
| post scriptum | P.S. | "written later" or postscript |

2. Marjorie added a ______________ at the end of her letter to remind Hector to write back soon.

3. The book written by Louis Gregory, ______________contains essays by all five of the authors.

4. The eruption of Mount Vesuvius buried the city of Pompeii in the year 79 _______.

5. Place commas where they are needed in the following sentence.

   With each flash of lightening Marta cried "The sky is on fire!"

6. Underline the adverb in this sentence. Which word does the adverb modify?

   Our team will play against the Westside Vikings tomorrow.

   ______________________________

7. Insert the correct homophone in each blank. road rode rowed

A) We ______________________ the canoe upstream until we reached the northern bank of the river.

B) We followed an unpaved __________________ on foot for a while.

C) Then we ________________________ in the back of a truck.

8. Use what you know about prefixes to answer the question. What is the source of hydroelectric power?

light water life weight

9. Cynthia used the book, Dolphins of the Deep Blue, by Tanya Overlook for her research paper. The book was published in Philadelphia by Islands Press in 2005. Look in the *Help Pages* to see how Cynthia should cite this article in her bibliography. Write the citation correctly below.

______________________________________________________________

10 – 12. Elise has made a list of bad habits, and her list has been revised to make three sentences that are grammatically correct. Rewrite the three correct sentences.

Some bad habbits (sp) are drinking too much, ~~and~~ doing drugs, ~~N~~not having any healthy foods for breakfast, lunch, and dinner. Smoking is really bad for you. ~~Having body odre is bad if you never shower.~~ ~~Never~~ Not washing your hair, streightening (sp) your hair too much, ~~is bad.~~ ~~B~~biting your nails, ~~N~~not washing your hands after going to the bathroom, and ~~S~~swareing (sp) ~~is also a~~ are all bad habits.

______________________________________________________________

______________________________________________________________

______________________________________________________________

______________________________________________________________

## Lesson #129

1. Choose the correct word to complete the sentence.

   The sunset over the ocean looked (beautiful / beautifully)!

2. Fill in the *verb of being* that agrees with the subject of this sentence.

   He and I _____ teammates a couple of years ago.

3. Sort this list of adjectives. Write each word next to its synonym.

   hilarious amusing insecure courageous humorous
   valiant uncertain heroic unstable

precarious ➡ ______________________________

comical ➡ ______________________________

brave ➡ ______________________________

4. Underline the word parts that have to do with "writing."

   -graph geo- -gram -script micro-

5. Check the spelling of these words. If a word is misspelled, cross it out and write it correctly on the line.

   commited traceable fateful

   ______________________________

6. This sentence states an opinion; rewrite it as a fact.

   Young people are not interested in proper nutrition or suitable exercise.

   ______________________________

7. Underline the action verb. Circle the direct object.

   Everyone gasped when Michelle dropped the ball.

8. Use these clauses to write a complex sentence.

snowed all night, classes were cancelled

______________________________________________

______________________________________________

9. Evaluate this sentence. If it needs improvement, rewrite it correctly.

The owners are him and me.

______________________________________________

10. **A subordinate clause must be used with a main clause to make a complete sentence.** Cross out the answer to the following question, and re-write the answer as a complete sentence.

Why aren't you going to the game? Because we don't have tickets.

______________________________________________

11. Which of these is an independent clause?

____ although I enjoy all kinds of ice cream

____ cookies 'n cream is my favorite flavor

12. Make a list of five linking verbs. Look in the *Help Pages* if you can't think of five.

______________

______________ ______________

______________ ______________

# Lesson #130

1. The word *lame* denotes a physical disability (as in "a lame horse"). This use of the term is considered offensive, if you are speaking about a person. However, *lame* also has a connotation: weak, inadequate, unsatisfactory (as in "a lame idea"). Look at each of the synonyms of *lame*. Write D if the word is a denotation of *lame*; write C if the word is a connotation of lame.

   ____ crippled ____ stupid ____ disabled

   ____ weak ____ substandard

2. Use a conjunction to join these sentences. Write the compound sentence.

   Jurina knows how to dance. Mattia can do the drumming.

   ______________________________

3. **The abbreviation *etc.* stands for the Latin words *et cetera*, which mean "and the rest" or "and so on."** This abbreviation should not be used in formal writing. Rewrite this sentence without the abbreviation.

   Please organize your books, notebooks, pencils, etc. neatly.

   ______________________________

4. **The word *done* is the past participle of *did*. It should never be used alone as a verb.** Rewrite this sentence correctly.

   I didn't want to make a collage because I done that before.

   ______________________________

5. Is the homograph a verb or a noun?

   In a desert the weather is hot and dry, but you may find some interesting vegetation.

   verb noun

6. Which word completes the analogy? *Niece* is to *nephew* as *daughter* is to ____.

   mother son aunt cousin

7. The Greek suffixes *–phobe* and *–phobia* mean "fear." There are many types of phobias such as claustrophobia or "fear of closed spaces." What does *photophobic* describe?

   A) fear of heights
   B) a type of puzzle
   C) an organism that avoids light
   D) love of sounds

8. Add commas to punctuate this sentence correctly.

   In Beijing China you can visit teahouses fairs and the Opera.

9. Shaun read Maury Peterson's article in the magazine, Artist Review. It was called "Painting Still Life," and was on pages 17 through 20 of the spring 2003, Volume 4 edition. Look in the *Help Pages* to see how Shaun should cite this article in his bibliography. Write the citation correctly below.

   ______________________________________________

**Proof It!** Michael is writing about classes that should be offered at his school. Read some of Michael's sentences below, and then complete items 10 – 12.

There are many classes at our school, but I think there should be more. I think there should be a german class. Because it would be chalenging. I also think there should be a longer computer class. Because everyone likes computers.

10. **Remember, a subordinate clause is not a complete sentence on its own.** Draw a line through two subordinating conjunctions that are used to begin sentences.

11. Underline two sentences that have no errors.

12. Use editing marks to correct a proper adjective that should be capitalized and to mark a spelling error.

## Lesson #131

**More Latin Phrases:** Many common American phrases are originally taken from Latin. Study the chart; then complete each of the following sentences with one of the phrases.

| Term | Meaning |
|---|---|
| antebellum | "before the war" |
| bona fide | "in good faith" |
| e pluribus unum | "one out of many" (Motto of the U.S.A.) |
| gratis | "without cost" or "out of kindness" |
| in absentia | "in their absence" |
| ad hoc | "for this purpose" |

1. The students formed an ______________________ committee strictly for the purpose of electing their candidate for class president.

2. Since many of the soldiers were serving overseas, they were able to vote ______________________ with absentee ballots.

3. The years preceding the American Civil War are known as the ______________________ years.

4. Underline the prepositional phrase.

   Put two drops of food coloring into the solution.

5. Choose the correct verb.

   The *British Broadcasting Company* usually (use / uses) the initials, BBC.

6. Underline two antonyms in this sentence.

   The wealthy citizens of our community often organize a fund-raiser to benefit disadvantaged children.

7. Choose the missing letters. ie ei

When the phone rings pick up the rec___ver.

8. Complete the sentence with a subject pronoun that agrees with the antecedent.

Both you and Sali should bring a snack, since __________ always get hungry after your workouts.

9. Is the room you are in right now very capacious? ____ Yes ____ No
If you're not sure, take a guess. Find a synonym for the underlined word in a dictionary or thesaurus, and write the synonym here.

______________________________

**What kind of sentence is it?** Write simple, compound, or complex to identify each of Brittany's sentences.

10. __________________ If I could be in charge for a day, there would be a longer recess and more activities each day.

11. __________________ I would let everyone eat outside, and nobody would have to wear uniforms.

12. __________________ We would get to watch movies almost all day long!

## Lesson #132

1. Are any of these plurals misspelled? Use a dictionary to check. Then write any misspelled words correctly.

   childrens sopranoes lice

   ______________________________

2. Below are some words that mean the "opposite of fat." Look in a dictionary or thesaurus to get more information about each word's specific connotation. Then, sort the words into positive and negative according to connotation; an example of each has been done for you.

   emaciated lean slender skinny undernourished

   scrawny slim gaunt willowy svelte

   Positive ➡ trim, ______________________________

   ______________________________

   Negative ➡ thin, ______________________________

   ______________________________

3. Add a comma after each interjection.

   Oh we are running late. Well at least the traffic isn't bad.

4. Underline the verb that agrees with the indefinite pronoun.

   Both (is / are) in the garage.

5. Look at the underlined homonyms. Write a V above the verb and an N above the noun.

   I cannot bear to see that bear in a cage!

6. Match these word parts with their meanings. *auto-* *anti-* *tri-*

   against ➡ __________ three ➡ __________ self ➡ __________

7. Place commas where they are needed in the following letter.

Dear Harry

Although you have been through some trying times it looks as though things are getting better for you. You have become famous for your wit creativity and good looks. Keep up the good work!

Respectfully

Sophia

8. Tricia interviewed her neighbor, a New York firefighter, for her report on careers. She interviewed Langston Hayes at his home on January 19, 2007. Look in the *Help Pages* to see how Tricia should cite this interview in her bibliography. Write the citation correctly below.

______________________________

______________________________

9. Complete the sentence by adding the past perfect form of the verb *hang*.

Last year, we __________ ______________ all the wreaths by Thanksgiving.

10. Underline the word that best completes the sentence.

When you get the ball, pass it to Dave or (I / me).

11. Which is a phrase and which is a clause? Write C or P.

____ the sled raced ____ down a very steep hill

12. Sort this list of adjectives. Write each word under its synonym. calm excellent outstanding peaceful hushed astonishing superior startling shocking

good ➡ ______________________________

surprising ➡ ______________________________

quiet ➡ ______________________________

# Lesson #133

1. Match each Latin term with its meaning below.

| | | | |
|---|---|---|---|
| A) | bona fide | _____ | without cost |
| B) | en masse | _____ | one out of many |
| C) | gratis | _____ | in a mass |
| D) | e pluribus unum | _____ | in good faith |

2. Read this sentence. The researchers studied many different types of bacteria. What is the action verb? What is the direct object?

action verb ➡ ______________ direct object ➡ ______________

3. Sort these nouns into four groups: persons, places, things, abstracts (ideas/qualities).

| | | | |
|---|---|---|---|
| Nelson | computer lab | Seattle | engagement |
| pillows | philosophy | Malawi | Suzie |

persons ➡ ______________________________

places ➡ ______________________________

things ➡ ______________________________

abstracts ➡ ______________________________

4. Underline the verb that agrees with the indefinite pronoun.

Several of the family members (visit / visits) the gravesite each year.

5. Write an F if the statement is a fact; write O if it is an opinion.

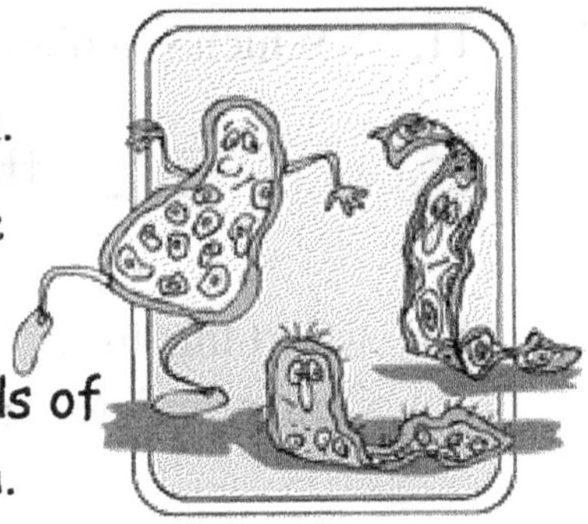

___ An epidemiologist is a scientist who studies the spread of diseases.

___ Epidemiology is one of the most important fields of research because of its impact on public health.

6. The fear of airplanes is called _____.

A) aviophobia B) aviation C) aviculture D) avocation

7. Complete the chart below by filling in the meaning of each symbol. Use the *Help Pages* if you are not sure what the symbols mean.

| Symbol | Meaning |
|---|---|
| @ | A) |
| ® | B) |
| © | C) |
| $ | D) |
| % | E) |
| & | F) |
| # | G) |

8. Complete the sentence by adding the future perfect form of the verb *hold.*

If Frederick keeps going, he __________ __________ __________ his breath for almost two minutes!

9. Find the meaning of the word *prolific* in a dictionary. Place a ✓ next to the statement that is true.

____ A prolific idea is not very creative.

____ A prolific writer has probably published many books or articles.

____ Prolific means the same as scarce.

10. Is the homograph a verb or an adjective? verb adjective

I sorted the items for our yard sale into four separate categories.

11. What does an imperative do?

tells something asks something gives a command shows strong feeling

12. Evaluate this sentence. If it needs improvement, rewrite it correctly.

The first people on the scene was us.

________________________________________

## Lesson #134

1. Look at the following pairs of words. The words are synonyms, but one has a positive connotation and the other has a negative connotation. Sort the words into two categories and write them in the chart below.

unusual, abnormal disabled, lame pigheaded, stubborn

smile, smirk emaciated, lean problematic, complex

| Positive | Negative |
|---|---|
| | |
| | |
| | |
| | |
| | |
| | |

2. What is the relative pronoun in this sentence? Write it. Underline its antecedent.

A clown who always wears a sad face did a performance in the square.

____________________

3. Match these subjects with their verbs.

| | |
|---|---|
| the choir | sing |
| the clergy | preaches |
| two vocalists | sings |

4. Have you seen this symbol? What does it stand for?

____________________________

5. Is the verb in the following sentence transitive or intransitive?

At the final buzzer everyone cheered like crazy!

transitive intransitive

6. Norris found information that he wants to use for his science report in the 2003 edition of Century Encyclopedia. The article is called "Tropical Fish," and is on pages 238 and 239 of Volume 11. Look in the *Help Pages* to see how Norris should cite this article in his bibliography. Write the citation correctly below.

______________________________________________

______________________________________________

Look at this sample index from a science text, and use it to answer the next two questions.

7. On what pages might you find information about how the moon affects the tides?

______________

8. On what pages would you find directions for making your own thermometer?

______________



9. Which is a phrase and which is a clause? Write C or P.

____ even if it rains ____ we will have fun

10 – 12. **Proof It!** Below are some sentences that Anna wrote. Read them, and underline the sentence that has no errors. Then, use editing marks to correct errors in the other sentences.

I think knowledge is better than money if you are stupid then you would waste your money on pointless things. If you are smart then you will proboubly make alot of money and spend it wisely. So, money is not better than knowledge!

# Lesson #135

1. Find these words in a dictionary. Underline the word that best completes the sentence.

   inquisitive inferior intrepid

   Although she was afraid, Abigail appeared ______ as she stood up to the bully.

2. Choose the verb and possessive pronoun that agree with the indefinite pronoun in this sentence.

   Somebody (has / have) forgotten (their / his) umbrella.

3. **You can use a semicolon to separate independent clauses.**
   **Example:** I'll go to the bank on Monday; I can do the shopping on Tuesday.
   Insert a semicolon in this sentence.

   The party starts at noon come early if you can.

4. Write the plural of *torpedo*.

   ______________________________

5. Write the abbreviation for *January*.

   ______________________________

6. Write the meanings of the abbreviations.

   Corp. ➡ _______________

   P.O. ➡ _______________ Rt. ➡ _______________

7. Choose the homophone that correctly completes the sentence.

   __________ are many ways to find information for your report.

   They're Their There

8. Underline two things that are compared in the simile.

Playing cards with Dahlia is like watching grass grow.

9. Write this book title correctly. my twenty first year

______________________________

Study the chart below and use it to answer items 10 – 12.

10. How are the states in this chart organized?

A) by population size

B) by geographical size

C) in alphabetical order

D) none of these

11. What important information is missing from this chart?

A) the title

B) the source of the information

C) the year of the census

D) the state capitals

Estimated Populations for Midwest States

| State | Estimated Population | Geographic Area in Square Miles |
|---|---|---|
| North Dakota | 636,677 | 70,704 |
| South Dakota | 775,933 | 77,121 |
| Montana | 935,670 | 147,046 |
| Minnesota | 5,132,799 | 86,943 |
| Wisconsin | 5,536,201 | 65,503 |
| Missouri | 5,800,310 | 69,709 |
| Kansas | 2,744,687 | 82,282 |
| Iowa | 2,966,334 | 56,276 |
| Indiana | 6,271,973 | 36,420 |
| Michigan | 10,120,860 | 96,810 |
| Ohio | 11,464,042 | 44,828 |
| Illinois | 12,763,371 | 57,918 |

Source: U. S. Census Bureau http://www.census.gov/

12. What can you conclude from the study of this chart?

A) The states with the largest geographic area also have the largest populations.

B) Most Americans live in the Midwest states.

C) The population of Illinois is roughly twice the population of North Dakota.

D) Three Midwest states have a population of less than one million each.

## Lesson #136

1. Look at the following pairs of words. The words are synonyms, but one has a less harsh connotation than the other. Sort the words into two categories and write them in the chart below.

irate, irritated | challenging, difficult | sneer, grin
distinctive, peculiar | inquisitive, probing | envy, admire

| Positive | Negative |
|---|---|
| | |
| | |
| | |
| | |
| | |
| | |

2. Match each abbreviation with its translation below.

| | |
|---|---|
| et. al. | that is to say |
| etc. | and the rest |
| i.e. | and others |

3. Underline the adverb and the verb it modifies.

Mom was looking everywhere for you!

4. Does the pronoun agree with its antecedent? Yes No

The crowd became quiet, and it responded to the speaker.

5. Complete the sentence by adding the present perfect form of the verb *spin*.

The artists ______________ ______________ many beautiful wall hangings and blankets.

6 – 12. Let's review the eight parts of speech. Complete the graphic organizer below by filling in whatever is missing. If you need help, use the *Help Pages*.

| | Part of Speech | Short Definition | Examples |
|---|---|---|---|
| A) | | modifies a noun or pronoun | |
| B) | | | in, onto, above, out, beside, under |
| C) | Noun | | |
| D) | | answers a question: how, where, when, or to what extent | |
| E) | | | Oh my! Wow! Hey! Ouch! Oh no! |
| F) | Pronoun | | |
| G) | | shows action or a state of being | |
| H) | | | and, or, so, but, nor |

## Lesson #137

**More Latin Phrases:** Here are more common American phrases, which are originally from Latin. Study the chart below; then complete each of the following sentences with one of the phrases.

| Term | Literal Meaning | Common Usage |
|---|---|---|
| per capita | "by heads" | per person |
| per diem | "by the day" | by the day |
| per se | "by itself" | in itself |
| ad infinitum | "to infinity" | endlessly |
| in memoriam | "to the memory of" | in memory |
| in toto | "in all" | completely |

1. Instead of a weekly salary, the laborers were paid ________________.

2. You can count by 2's to a hundred, a thousand, and ________________.

3. When my grandfather died, many people made generous donations

   ________________________.

4. Choose the correct predicate adjective.

   That baby is so (loud / loudly)!

5. Choose the verb that agrees.

   Comic books (is / were) my favorite birthday gift.

6. Which of these is an antonym for the word *aghast*?

   stunned horrified amazed unconcerned

7. Karina found information that she wants to use for her history report in the 2003 edition of Knowledge Encyclopedia. The article is called "The New Deal," and is on pages 222 - 225 of Volume 8. Look in the *Help Pages* to see how Karina should cite this article in her bibliography. Write the citation correctly below.

_______________________________________________

8. Underline the fact.

In many public and private schools, students are required to wear uniforms. Student uniforms make life easier for parents and teachers, but the students resent having to wear them.

9. What is the direct object in this sentence? ____________

Mr. Harvey disciplined the whole class for our behavior at lunch yesterday.

Read Chelsea's writing sample and then make the corrections listed below.

A cartoon character that I like is Jerry the Mouse, from Tom and Jerry, the TV show. Jerry is so smart! He always outsmarts tom, and he teaches his nefew to do the same. What Jerry does that I like is that he uses his surroundings. He can almost always find something around him that he can use.

10. The title of a television show should be underlined.

11. Mark a spelling error.

12. Mark a capitalization error.

## Lesson #138

1. All of the words listed below mean "out of the ordinary." But the words have different connotations. Think about the connotation of each word or look in a dictionary or thesaurus to get more information about each word. Sort the words into positive and negative according to connotation.

exceptional unique odd unusual bizarre
distinctive weird abnormal strange special

| Positive | Negative |
|---|---|
| | |
| | |
| | |
| | |
| | |
| | |

2. Fill in the conjunction that best completes the sentence.

Both my sister ________ Aunt Mira have reddish hair.

3. Choose the verbs that agree with the collective nouns.

My mom's firm (sponsor / sponsors) Family Field Day every year, and my dad's company (provide / provides) all the prizes.

4. Complete the sentence by adding the past perfect form of the verb *spin*.

Charlotte ____________ ____________ a web for her babies while Wilbur wasn't paying attention.

5. Underline all the nouns in this sentence.

Libby and her husband hosted a party at the lake to celebrate the marriage of Michael and Katie.

6. Underline the indefinite pronoun, and choose the verb that agrees.

Little (was / were) done to repair the damaged roads.

7. Underline two antonyms in this sentence.

Martha is usually very precise, but her figures on this report are inaccurate.

8. The action verb is in bold print. Underline the direct object.

Sean had **sunk** four baskets by the end of the first quarter.

9. Choose the word that completes this analogy.

*Columbus* is to *Ohio* as *Harrisburg* is to ___________.

Pennsylvania New York Georgia Kentucky

Write the past, present participle, and past participle of each verb.

| | Present | Past | Present Participle | Past Participle |
|---|---|---|---|---|
| 10. | knock | | | |
| 11. | arrive | | | |
| 12. | recover | | | |

## Lesson #139

1. Underline the object of the preposition.

   Hester kicked the ball across the field.

2. The following sentence contains either a simile or a metaphor. Which is it? What are the two things being compared?

   The sight of him made my heart leap like a bullfrog that has just been startled out of a sound sleep.

   simile metaphor ______________________________

3. Choose the verbs that agree.

   All of the dancers (is / are) here, but none of them (have / has) had their auditions yet.

4. Imagine that you are working on a geography report. What should you do in order to avoid plagiarism?

   A) Copy from a friend.
   B) Use a variety of sources and list them in a bibliography.
   C) Download a paper from the internet.
   D) all of these

5. Underline the verb(s). Write past, present, or future. ______________

   In June we will be promoted to seventh grade.

6. Improve this sentence by finding a synonym for the underlined verb; write your verb on the line.

   Nathan was so distraught when his mother left, he <u>cried</u> all afternoon.

   ______________________________

7. Underline the predicate nominative.

   Patricia is the Director of Human Resources.

8. Complete the sentence by adding the future perfect form of the verb *sleep*.

If you go to bed now, you ______________ ______________

______________ a good eight hours by the time your alarm goes off.

9. Complete the chart.

| Present | Past | Present Participle | Past Participle |
|---|---|---|---|
| make | made | is making | had made |
| receive | | | |
| unpack | | | |

10. During World War II, the Women's Army Corps was known as the WAC. WAC's served as medical technicians and secretaries, but they were never in direct combat.

A) What acronym is used in the sentences above? ______________

B) Are the sentences factual or do they state someone's opinion?

factual opinion

11. Choose the verb and possessive pronoun that agree with the indefinite pronoun.

Today, everybody (get / gets) a chance to launch (his / their) bottle rocket!

12. Which word is the direct object in the sentence above?

A) bottle B) everybody C) Today D) rocket

## Lesson #140

1. Choose the word with the "softest" connotation.

   William owns hundreds of out-of-print books;

   he has a (unique / bizarre) collection.

2. Match each Latin expression with its meaning below.

   A) per capita ____ completely

   B) per se ____ to infinity, endlessly

   C) in toto ____ by each person

   D) ad infinitum ____ by, of, or for itself

3. Add the proper punctuation to this interjection within a quote.

   Yikes cried the pitcher.

4. Look at the underlined verb. Is it a linking verb, an action verb, or a helping verb?

   The track and field day activities seemed rigorous this year!

   linking verb action verb helping verb

5. Which two are antonyms? Use a dictionary to check your guess.

   prominent lively miniature unknown

6. Is this sentence simple, compound, or complex?

   Even though we made some money, I never want to baby-sit again!

   simple compound complex

7. Choose the correct verb.

   You and I (am / was / were) the only graduates in the room.

8. What is the tense of the verbs in the following sentence?

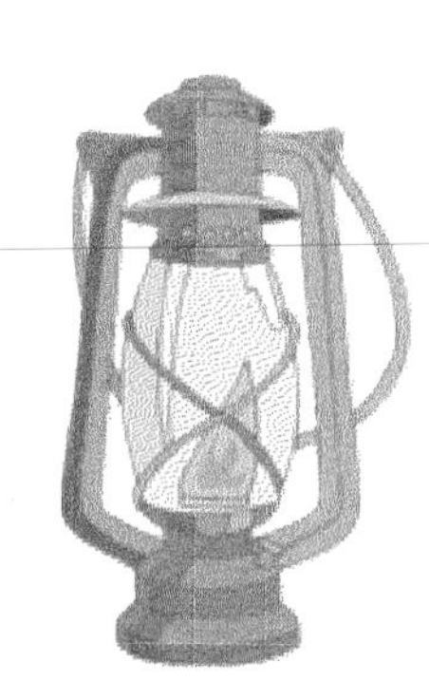

With the lantern, we will have lighting even if the power goes out.

present past future

9. One way to measure the wealth of a country is through <u>per capita income</u>. What is *per capita income*? (Look back at Lesson #137 if you need help.)

______________________________________________

10 – 12. **Perfect Tenses** The perfect tenses all use a form of the verb *to have* with the past participle. Complete the chart below.

| | Present perfect | Past Perfect | Future Perfect |
|---|---|---|---|
| Helping Verb | *has or have* | *had* | *will have* |
| A) | have sat | | |
| B) | | had heard | |
| C) | | | will have carried |
| D) | | had spun | |
| E) | has taught | | |
| F) | | | will have done |

# Simple Solutions

English Grammar & Writing Mechanics

level 6

## Help Pages

# Help Pages

| The Eight Parts of Speech | |
|---|---|
| **Adjectives** modify nouns or pronouns. A proper adjective begins with a capital letter. | |
| **Adverbs** modify verbs, adjectives, or other adverbs. Adverbs tell how, when, where, and to what extent. For lists of common adverbs, see below. | |
| Adverbs that tell *How* – see Lesson 43 | Adverbs that tell *Where* – see Lessons 50, 82 |
| Adverbs that tell *When* – see Lesson 54 | Adverbs that tell *To What Extent* – see Lesson 66 |
| **Conjunctions** connect similar words, clauses, or phrases within a sentence. | |
| **Coordinate Conjunctions**: and, or, nor, but, yet, for, so | |
| **Subordinating Conjunctions** join a subordinate clause with a main clause. See Lesson 58 for a list. | |
| **Correlative Conjunctions** act in pairs. See list of examples below. either/or, neither/nor, both/and, whether/or, not/but, not only/but also | |
| **Interjections** are words or phrases that express strong feeling. **Examples:** Wow! Oh, no! Look! | |
| **Nouns** name a person, place, thing, or idea. Nouns may be common or proper, singular or plural. A proper noun begins with a capital letter. | |
| **Collective Nouns** are words that name a "collection." A collective noun is singular and is treated as a single unit. Collective nouns used as subjects take *singular verbs*. **Examples:** the team *is*, the troupe *plays*, a class *studies*, my family *enjoys* | |
| **Prepositions** relate nouns or pronouns to other words in the sentence. For a list of common prepositions, see chart below. | |
| A **Prepositional phrase** begins with a preposition and ends with a noun or a pronoun. See Lessons 28 – 32. | |
| **Pronouns** replace nouns. The pronoun *I* is always capitalized. Common pronoun types are described on p. 288. | |
| **Verbs** convey action or a state of being. A verb is the main word in the predicate of a sentence. For an explanation of verb types, see p. 287. | |

| Some Common Prepositions: | | | | | |
|---|---|---|---|---|---|
| about | around | by | into | over | under |
| above | before | down | near | out | underneath |
| across | behind | during | nearby | outside | until |
| after | below | except | next to | past | up |
| against | beneath | for | of | through | upon |
| along | beside | from | off | throughout | with |
| alongside | between | in | on | to | within |
| among | beyond | inside | onto | toward | without |

# Help Pages

| Editing Marks: | |
|---|---|
| Capital letter | ≡ |
| End punctuation | ⊙ ⓘ ⓘ |
| Add something | ∧ |
| Change to lower case | / |
| Take something out | ℘ |
| Check spelling | sp ◯ |
| Indent | ¶ |

| Common Keyboard Symbols | |
|---|---|
| **Symbol** | **Meaning** |
| @ | at |
| ® | trademark |
| © | copyright |
| $ | dollars |
| % | percent |
| & | and |
| # | pounds or number |

| Rules for using Brackets, Colons, Semicolons, Dashes, & Hyphens: | |
|---|---|
| **Brackets** [ ] are used in dictionary definitions or to insert words into writing that is already within parentheses. Brackets are always used in pairs. | |
| **Colons:** | 1. A colon (:) is used between the hour and minutes, or between minutes and seconds when writing the time.<br>**Examples:** At around 12:30, we eat lunch.<br>My running time was 13:35 (13 minutes and 35 seconds). |
| | 2. A colon may be used after the greeting in a formal or business letter. |
| | 3. A colon may be used before a list of items, but only after an independent clause.<br>Incorrect ➔ I have traveled to: Russia, Italy, Iran, and Cuba.<br>Correct ➔ I have visited many countries: Russia, Italy, Iran, and Cuba. |
| | 4. A colon may be used before a long quote or if there is no other introduction, such "he said" or "she replied."<br>**Example:** Martha looked up at George: "Where have you been all day?" |
| **Semicolons:** | 1. A semicolon (;) may be used to separate two independent clauses with no conjunction. The semicolon takes the place of a comma or conjunction.<br>Incorrect ➔ You can come in now; but please sit quietly.<br>Correct ➔ You can come in now; please sit quietly. |
| | 2. Use a semicolon to separate items in a series if there are already commas in the items.<br>**Example:** Lorain, Ohio; New Castle, Pennsylvania; and Chicago, Illinois |
| **Dashes** (–) are used between words within sentences. A dash is longer than a hyphen and is used to show emphasis. A dash should be used for a special effect – do not overuse it. | |

# Help Pages

## Rules for using Brackets, Colons, Semicolons, Dashes, & Hyphens:

**Hyphens:**

1. A hyphen (-) is used between the tens and the ones place, when writing out the numbers twenty-one through ninety-nine.
   **Examples:** seventy-six, forty-eight
2. A hyphen is used when writing fractions.
   **Examples:** four-fifths, one-third, three-eighths
3. A hyphen is used to separate words on two lines. (It is best to avoid separation of words in this way. Furthermore, the hyphen can only be used between syllables.)
4. A hyphen is sometimes used to join a prefix with a base word. The hyphen helps to make the word more clear.
   **Examples:** re-evaluate, non-military, ex-girlfriend
5. Hyphens are used in some compound words.
   **Examples:** part-time, president-elect, father-in-law
6. Words are changing, and are being added to the English language, constantly. Therefore, always use an up-to-date dictionary to verify whether or not a word can/should be hyphenated.

## Rules for using Commas:

1. Use commas to separate words or phrases in a series.
   **Example:** Sun brought a coloring book, some crayons, a pair of scissors, and a ruler.
2. Use a comma to separate two independent clauses joined by a conjunction.
   **Example:** Dad works in the city, and he is a commuter.
3. Use a comma after an introductory word, such as an interjection.
   **Example:** Hey, who wants to play tennis?
   Do not use a comma if there is an end mark after the interjection.
   **Example:** Oh no! It's starting to rain.
4. Use a comma to separate two words or two numbers, when writing a date.
   **Example:** Friday, April 7, 2006
5. Use commas between adjectives if the order doesn't matter.
   **Example:** the exciting, fresh dance moves
   (This could also read fresh, exciting dance moves or exciting *and* fresh dance moves.)
6. Do not use commas between adjectives that describe in different ways.
   **Example:** three green tomatoes (*Three* tells how many, and *green* describes the color.)
7. Insert a comma after introductory words or phrases in a sentence.
   **Example:** On the other hand, you may not need any help.
8. Use commas before and after "interrupting phrases" within a sentence.
   **Example:** Ms. Cole, *the bank teller*, was very helpful.
9. Use commas before and/or after contrasting phrases that use *not*.
   **Example:** I worked on my science project, *not my essay*, all evening.

# Help Pages

## Sentences:

**Sentence Types:** Declarative, Exclamatory, Interrogative, and Imperative – See Lesson 2.

| Structure | Parts | Joined by | Example |
|---|---|---|---|
| Simple | subject & predicate only | --- | We will hold a rally at the local park. |
| Compound | two independent clauses | conjunction (and, but, or) | There will be speeches in the morning, *and* we will play games in the afternoon. |
| Complex | subordinate and main clause | subordinating conjunction | The rally will last until dusk *unless* the weather is severe. |

## Verbs:

**Action Verbs** show action.

**Transitive Verbs** are action verbs that send action to a direct object.

**Example:** A stunt man *performs* dangerous *feats.*
(verb ➧ performs; direct object ➧ feats)

**Intransitive Verbs** are action verbs that have no direct object.

**Example:** The symphony performs every Sunday.
(verb ➧ performs; no direct object)

**Verbs of Being (Forms of *be*)** do not show action; they can act as linking or helping verbs.

is, are, was, were, be, am, being, been

**Linking Verbs** do not show action; they show a condition.

**Examples:** appear, become, feel, seem, smell, taste, sounds, and all forms of *be.*

**Auxiliary (Helping) Verbs** are used with other verbs to form a verb phrase.

**Examples:** is, are, was, were, be, am, being, been, might, could, should, would, can, do, does, did, may, must, will, shall, have, has, had

**Verb Tense** tells the time when the action or condition of the verb occurs. The basic verb tenses are past, present, and future. There are also three perfect verb tenses in English; they all use past tense verbs, plus the helping verbs, *had*, *has*, or *have*.

| | Present Perfect | Past Perfect | Future Perfect |
|---|---|---|---|
| **Use of the Verb** | Shows action that is ongoing or indefinite. | Shows which thing happened first. (Both things already happened.) | Shows what will happen before something else in the future. |
| **Helping Verbs** | *has* or *have* | *had* | *will have* |
| **Example with singular subject** | Nick *has finished* two of his assignments. | She *had asked* for help before she began working. | I *will have completed* my chores by bedtime. |
| **Example with plural subject** | We *have played* soccer for five years. | The children *had napped* earlier that afternoon. | They *will have learned* the routines by then. |

# Help Pages

| Pronouns: |
| --- |
| **Demonstrative Pronouns** -- used to point out something. this, that, these, those<br>Demonstratives can also be adjectives. **Examples:** this house, these coins |
| **Indefinite Pronouns** replace nouns that are not specific.<br>Singular - see Lesson 37; Plural - see Lesson 38; Singular or Plural - see Lesson 39. |
| **Interrogative Pronouns** -- used to ask a question. what, which, who, whom, whose |
| **Nominative Pronouns** -- used as the subject or as a predicate nominative.<br>I, you, he, she, it, we, you, they |
| **Object Pronouns** -- used in the predicate as a direct object or an object of a preposition.<br>me, you, him, her, it, us, them |
| **Possessive Pronouns** show ownership. Some possessive pronouns are used with nouns:<br>my, your, his, her, its, our, your, their, and whose.<br>Other possessive pronouns can stand alone:<br>hers, his, mine, ours, theirs, yours, and whose. |
| **Relative Pronouns** -- used to relate a clause to an antecedent: that, which, who, whom, and whose. |

| Spelling Rules: |
| --- |
| **Rules for Forming Plurals:** |
| 1. Words ending in *s*, *x*, *z*, *ch*, or *sh*, add *-es* to make the plural. |
| 2. Many words that end in *-f* or *-fe* form the plural by changing the *-f* or *-fe* to *-ves*. (thief ➡ thieves) Some nouns that end in *-f* or *-ff* do not follow the rule for making plurals. (cliff ➡ cliffs, belief ➡ beliefs) |
| 3. Some nouns that end in a consonant + *-o* form the plural by adding *-s* (zero ➡ zeros); others add *-es* . (tomato ➡ tomatoes) |
| 4. Irregular plural nouns have a completely different spelling in the plural form. (ox ➡ oxen, goose ➡ geese, louse ➡ lice) |
| **Other Spelling Rules:** |
| 5. Place *i* before *e*, except after *c*, or when sounded like *ā* as in ***neighbor*** and ***weigh***. (mischief, eight) |
| 6. Regular verbs show past tense by adding *-ed*. (stop ➡ stopped) Irregular verbs change their spelling in the past tense. See "Irregular Verbs" on p. 289. |
| 7. When adding a prefix to a word, do not change the spelling of the prefix or the root. (mis- + step ➡ misstep) |
| 8. If a word ends in a vowel and *-y*, add a suffix without changing the spelling of the word. (employ + -er ➡ employer) |
| 9. If a word ends in a consonant + *-y*, change the *y* to *i* before adding suffixes such as *-es*, *-er*, *-ed*, or *-est*. (try ➡ tried) If the suffix begins with an *-i*, do not change the *-y* to *-i*. (hurry ➡ hurrying) |
| 10. There are many exceptions to spelling rules. If you are not sure of the spelling of a word, use a dictionary to check. |

# Help Pages

**Irregular Verbs:**

| Present | Past | With *has, have,* or *had* |
|---|---|---|
| bear | bore | *has, have,* or *had* born |
| bite | bit | *has, have,* or *had* bitten |
| bleed | bled | *has, have,* or *had* bled |
| buy | bought | *has, have,* or *had* bought |
| cling | clung | *has, have,* or *had* clung |
| deal | dealt | *has, have,* or *had* dealt |
| feel | felt | *has, have,* or *had* felt |
| flee | fled | *has, have,* or *had* fled |
| forgive | forgave | *has, have,* or *had* forgiven |
| grind | ground | *has, have,* or *had* ground |
| hear | heard | *has, have,* or *had* heard |
| hold | held | *has, have,* or *had* held |
| lie | lay | *has, have,* or *had* lain |
| light | lit/lighted | *has, have,* or *had* lit/lighted |
| overtake | overtook | *has, have,* or *had* overtaken |
| overthrow | overthrown | *has, have,* or *had* overthrown |
| shine | shone | *has, have,* or *had* shone |
| sit | sat | *has, have,* or *had* sat |
| sleep | slept | *has, have,* or *had* slept |
| slide | slid | *has, have,* or *had* slid |
| spin | spun | *has, have,* or *had* spun |
| string | strung | *has, have,* or *had* strung |

**Prefixes, Suffixes, and Roots** (Oh my!)

| | Meaning | | Meaning | | Meaning | | Meaning |
|---|---|---|---|---|---|---|---|
| *able* | able to | *con* | with | *less* | without | *phobia* | fear |
| *amphi* | both | *chrono* | time | *im, in* | not | *phone* | sound |
| *ante* | before | *de* | take away | *inter* | between | *photo* | light |
| *anthropo* | human | *di* | two | *mal* | evil | *port* | carry |
| *anti* | against | *dia* | across | *micro* | tiny | *post* | after |
| *auto* | self | *dict* | speak | *mis* | badly | *pre* | before |
| *biblio* | book | *dis* | not | *mono* | one | *re* | again |
| *bi* | two | *ful* | full of | *morph* | form | *scrib* | write |
| *bio* | life | *geo* | earth | *neo* | new | *script* | write |
| *bronte* | thunder | *graph, gram* | written | *non* | not | *thermo* | heat |
| *centri* | center | *hemi* | half | *ology* | study of | *trans* | across |
| *circum* | around | *hydro* | water | *ped* | foot | *tri* | three |
| *co, com* | with | *ible* | able | *phobe* | fear | *un* | not |

# Help Pages

## Bibliography:

A bibliography lists sources in alphabetical order. The author's name, title of the book, magazine, or internet article is included, as well as the publisher, date of publication, and sometimes page numbers. Most teachers prefer to have students set up a bibliography in a certain way. You should follow your teacher's directions for setting up a bibliography, according to what is required at your school. Here are some guidelines and examples of how to list various sources.

**Book:**

Author's last name, first name. Title of Book. City: Publisher, Date.

**Example:**

Lawry, Matthew. Fascinating Desert Life Forms. Dayton: Traders Press, 2004.

**Encyclopedia:**

Title of Encyclopedia, Date. Volume Number, "Title of Article," page numbers.

**Example:**

Universe Encyclopedia, 2006. Vol. 3, "Deserts," pp. 19-23.

**Magazine Article:**

Author's last name, first name, "Article Title." Name of Magazine. Volume Number, (Date): page numbers.

**Example:**

Phillips, Carla, "My Days in the Sahara." Geography and More. Vol. 18, No. 3, (Fall 2000): pp. 3-5.

**Internet Article:**

Author's name, (Date). Title. Electronic Forum (Online). Email address, if available.

**Example:**

Tasha Green, (March 9, 2004). Desert Life. Topics to Research (Online). homeworkhelp@singleton.com, 2006.

**World Wide Web:**

URL. Author or name of item, date.

**Example:**

http://www.learnaboutdeserts.com. Lisa King, June 1, 2006.

**Personal Interview:**

Person's last name, first name. Occupation. Date of interview.

**Example:**

Journeyman, James. Zoologist. February 20, 2007.

## Figures of Speech:

| | |
|---|---|
| **Simile** | A simile is a way to describe something by using a comparison. A simile compares two things using the words *like* or *as*. **Example:** The baby is *as playful as a kitten*. The baby is being compared to a kitten. See Lesson 10. |
| **Metaphor** | A metaphor compares two things, but does not use *like* or *as*. It uses a form of the verb *be*. **Example:** Joey is a magnet for bad luck. See Lessons 13, 15. |

| | | | |
|---|---|---|---|
| **Denotation** | See Lesson 85. | **Connotation** | See Lesson 2. |